LIBR

MENLO SCHOOL AN

D0484079

Man: HIS FIRST MILLION YEARS

Man: HIS FIRST MILLION YEARS

by

Ashley Montagu

THE WORLD PUBLISHING COMPANY

CLEVELAND AND NEW YORK

Published by The World Publishing Company
2231 West 110th Street, Cleveland 2, Ohio

Published simultaneously in Canada by
Nelson, Foster & Scott Ltd.

Library of Congress Catalog Card Number: 57-9280

FIRST EDITION

Figure 11 modified from an illustration in A History of Technology, *Vol. 1, ed. by Charles Singer, E. J. Holmyard, and A. R. Hall, Oxford: Oxford University Press, 1954.*
Figures 14, 16, and 19 reproduced by permission, from Man the Tool-Maker *by K. P. Oakley, London: British Museum (Natural History), 1956.*
Figure 22 modified from an illustration in An Introduction to Physical Anthropology *by Ashley Montagu, Springfield, Ill.: C C Thomas, 1951.*
All other illustrations are by Charles Gottlieb and Herbert Marcelin.
The quotations on pages 195–197 and 201–202 are from Primitive Man as Philosopher *by Paul Radin, copyright Appleton-Century, New York.*

WP 757
Copyright © 1957 by Ashley Montagu.
All rights reserved. No part of this book may be reproduced in any form without written permission from the publisher, except for brief passages included in a review appearing in a newspaper or magazine. Printed in the United States of America.

TO *Alexander Cheyne*

Contents

Meganthropus palaeojavanicus · *Pithecanthropus erectus* · *Pithecanthropus robustus* · Solo Man · *Sinanthropus pekinensis* · *Atlanthropus mauritanicus* · Wadjak Man · Rhodesian Man · Heidelberg Man · Neanderthal Man · Early Mixtures of Different Types of Men · Cro-Magnon Man

CONTENTS

Illustrations

ILLUSTRATIONS

Tables

Preface

THIS BOOK has been written for people who want to learn, no matter what their chronological age may be—people who find their interest in life steadily increasing and who expect to find it continuously so. By "interest" I don't mean the enthusiasm of the moment but the intense and enduring interest of a lifetime.

It seems to me that anthropology should form a part of the equipment of every person who enjoys the benefit of a high school education. Indeed, I believe that anthropology should form the core of the educational curriculum at all levels, grammar school, high school, and college. I know of no public high school in which anthropology is taught as a regular course, but there are already a handful of private schools in which it is so taught—and with great success. I hope the example of these schools will be widely imitated. Meanwhile, those who desire a simple, uncomplicated introduction to anthropology may find the present book helpful.

Human beings are, surely, the most interesting creatures on the face of the earth, yet, strangely enough, their study has been almost the very last of the sciences to come into being. Anthropology, the science of man, is just about the youngest of the sciences, and it is, without any doubt, the most important —the most important because it deals with humanity itself, with the great questions of life and of death. What is man? What is he born as? What is he born for? Where did he come from? Whither has he been going? How did he come to present so many different types, both physically and culturally? These, and many more, are some of the questions which anthropology asks and attempts to answer. There can be scarcely any questions more important than these, unless it be the question: In what direction should man go? Here, I think, anthropology is in a position to return some fundamental answers, for if one would know what man is born *for,* one ought to begin by learning what he is born *as.*

There are some anthropologists who declare that it is not the business of anthropology to tell anyone what he was born for. The scientist, they say, should not be concerned with value judgments, with distinguishing between what *is* and what is *desirable* and then going on to recommend the desirable. The scientist's job, they claim, should be to discover what *is*; as for what *should be*, that can be left to the individual or to philosophers. It is further argued that one cannot draw any inferences or seek a direction from what is for what should be. This is a point of view with which I do not agree. I think one can and should study man in order to learn what he is so that we may the better be able to make him what he should be. Knowledge for the sake of knowledge is all very well, but where man is concerned we need to apply the findings of science to the problems he creates. That way we may eventually accomplish the realization of the best that is in everyone, for the maximization of their own and their fellow human beings' happiness.

I have developed this point of view, in the light of scientific evidence, in my book *The Direction of Human Development* (Harper & Brothers, New York, 1955). In the present volume I have adhered principally to the statement of the facts of anthropology. The reader will, I expect, be able to go on from them to the proper conclusions. And so let us begin.

ASHLEY MONTAGU

20 June 1957
Princeton, N. J.

Man: HIS FIRST MILLION YEARS

1

Introducing Ourselves

MAY I HAVE the pleasure of introducing you to yourself? Please meet *Homo sapiens,* meaning "man the wise," the most interesting creature on the face of the earth. The most interesting, the most exciting, the most promising. Did you know you were all that, and a great deal more, with special emphasis on the "more"?

Before we go a step further, please note that when reference is made to man throughout this book, woman is also included, and not merely as an afterthought, either—as we shall see. When the sexes are to be distinguished, the usage will be clear enough.

Let us resume where we broke off. Why is man the most interesting, the most exciting, and the most promising of all the creatures on the face of the earth? Isn't it rather self-conceited to speak of ourselves in such a manner? There are some who think that it is. These are the people who think that man is a vulgar, oafish upstart who, with consummate arrogance and in the worst possible taste, has assumed the name of *Homo sapiens.* They feel that the appellation *sapiens,* the wisdom part, has yet to be earned. It is interesting to note that most of these people would not deny that man could deserve to be called wise if he tried.

The name *Homo sapiens* ("Homo" stands for the zoological *genus,* and "sapiens" for the zoological *species*) was first given to man as a zoological group by the great Swedish botanist and systematist Karl von Linné (1707–78), known to the world, and later referred to in this book, by the Latinized form of his name, Linnaeus. When he named man *Homo sapiens,* he wanted to make it quite clear that the distinguishing mark of man was his ability to use his mind, an ability in which the human species undoubtedly far surpasses all other creatures. In this sense we, as a species, are well named. Without any self-conceit it is very desirable for us to understand ourselves for what we are, for the better we know ourselves, the better we shall be able to realize our potentialities. As human beings we are the most interesting creatures on the face of the earth because we are the most interested. The best way to be interesting is to be interested in some thing or things; then you can't help but be interesting to other people. There is no limit to the interest of human beings, an interest which is often called curiosity. Man is the most curious of all creatures. He is always wanting to find out. He is the Nosy Parker of Creation. With his curiosity he has conquered land, sea, and air; he has split the atom, tunneled the earth, reduced space to a fraction of time, created radio, television. Through his outstanding representatives, he has given us all the beauty of poetry, the drama, great books, painting, the dance—all art, indeed—great thoughts, and greatest of all, great lives, as those of the Chinese sage Confucius (551?– 479? B.C.), the Indian religious leader Buddha (563?–483?

B.C.), Christ (6 B.C.?–29 A.D.?), the fountainhead of Christianity, and in our own time such men and women as Gandhi (1869–1948), the great Indian leader, Albert Schweitzer (1875–   ), Florence Nightingale (1820–1910), "the Lady with the Lamp," modernizer of nursing and hospital administration, and Susan Anthony (1820–1906), the great reformer and leader of the woman suffrage movement.

This book, in fact, would not be large enough to hold all the names of those human beings who have earned, by their achievements, the title of "great." Every people has had its great ones, and the names of most of these have been forgotten. Recorded history is no more than six thousand years old, whereas human beings have been making history ever since they have been on this earth, a period believed to be about one million years. The long period of human experience before recorded, or *written,* history begins, is known as prehistory or the prehistoric period. Very few great names have come down to us from that period, and yet we can be certain that there were men quite as great living in the periods of prehistory as there have been in the historic period.

If we seem to know more than our ancestors did, it is not because we have brains that are more highly developed, but because we have inherited all that they have bequeathed to us in the form of knowledge and wisdom. We can see farther ahead and over a wider territory not because we have better eyes, but because standing as it were, on their shoulders we can see more—but if it were not for their shoulders we would be able to see no more than they were able to see. Oftentimes we are not able to see as much, for, casting our vision over so broad an expanse of territory, we often miss the things that are closest to our noses. That is why, every so often, it is a good thing to hang a question mark on the things we take most for granted. Since some of the things men take for granted are likely to be wrong and some right, it is highly desirable that every society encourage the inquiring mind. If we are ever to distinguish between the right and the wrong, we shall most efficiently be able to do so through unimpassioned inquiry. Happily man is the most inquiring creature in creation, so we needn't worry. We should begin to worry only when obstacles are created to prevent men from pursuing their inquiries in freedom and without restraint.

Being as interested as he is in the world around him, man, from the earliest times, has learned to make use of his environment in so rich a variety of ways that were one to spend the whole of one's life trying to learn about them, one could acquire knowledge of only a small segment of them. Man has greatly added to his own intrinsic interest by the way in which he has improved upon or added to the environments in which he has found himself. But he is also interesting because of what the environment has done by way of improving him, producing all the wonderful varieties in which we find man today both as a physical and as a social creature. But, then, this is what this book is mostly going to be about.

That man is the most exciting of all creatures is, in part, due to his peculiar faculty for adventuring into unexplored territories. Now that so much of the earth has been explored, he is beginning to turn his attention to the exploration of interplanetary space. The future of man in a world served by the harnessed atom is most exciting to contemplate. Mechanical brains, mechanical factories, muscle power outmoded, the increase of leisure, longer life, peace and good will on earth unto all men—the horizons are unlimited! It is good, and the highest of all privileges, to be a member of the species *Homo sapiens*.

The promise of *Homo sapiens* is such that we have but to apply what we already know about his nature to make virtual heaven upon this earth for everyone. *Homo sapiens* is the most educable of all living things—which means that he can learn quite as many wrong things about himself as right ones, and hence confuse himself very much more efficiently than any other creature. Man at the present time, in many parts of the earth, is seriously suffering from such confusion. And we men of the Western world are suffering from this confusion in many ways, perhaps as much as people anywhere else in the world.

In order to make clear in our minds the causes of this confusion—and it is only by doing so that we will extricate ourselves from it—it is necessary to learn what we can of the ways in which, and the routes by which, we came to be as we now are. The body of organized knowledge which deals with this very subject is called anthropology, the science of man, surely the most interesting science that one could possibly study.

2

Introducing Anthropology

ANTHROPOLOGY is the science of man. That's a pretty broad definition. Let's try to draw a line around it so that we can really grasp what the science is concerned with. The word "anthropology" is derived from two Greek words, the one *anthropos* meaning "man," and the other *logos* meaning "ordered knowledge." So anthropology is the ordered knowledge of man. The fact is that anything relating to man is grist to the anthropologist's mill. Anthropology is divided into two great divisions: (1) cultural anthropology, and (2) physical anthropology.

Cultural Anthropology

Cultural anthropology is concerned with the study of man's cultures. By "culture" the anthropologist understands what may be called the man-made part of the environment: the pots and pans, the laws and institutions, the art, religion, philosophy. Whatever a particular group of people living together as a functioning population have learned to do as human beings, their way of life, in short, is to be regarded as culture. The cultural anthropologist studies different cultures and compares them with one another in order to learn how it is that people come to do what they do in so many different ways, and also to learn, wherever possible, the relationships of one culture to another. He tries to find those common elements in all cultures which can be summarized in terms of generalizations or laws which are true of all cultures. Where there are differences, he tries to find the causes of these differences.

The cultural anthropologist is interested in all the forms that human social behavior assumes in organized societies. He cannot remain contented with the mere description of these forms, for he desires to understand how they have come into being, and so the cultural anthropologist must often be quite as good a psychologist as he is anything else. Fundamentally what he is really interested in is the nature of human nature. Today there is quite a flourishing school of anthropologists known as the personality-in-culture school. These cultural anthropologists, such as Margaret Mead, Clyde Kluckhohn, John Honigmann, Francis Hsu, and many others, are interested in tracing the relationship of the cultures in which human beings are socialized, that is, brought up, to the kind of personalities they develop.

Other cultural anthropologists are interested as specialists in studying such aspects of the cultures of different peoples as their legal institutions, social organization, religion, mythology, language, and their material culture such as their art, pottery, basketry, implements, and the like. Some cultural anthropologists take whole tribes for their special study and spend from many months to many years attempting to study every aspect of their culture.

Traditionally the cultural anthropologist has studied the so-called "primitive peoples" of this earth, and the major part of the anthropologist's attention still continues to be devoted to the cultures of such peoples, but in more recent years anthropologists have been turning their attention to the study of the technologically more advanced peoples of the earth. Today we have good anthropological studies not only of the Australian aborigines and the Congo pygmies, but also of the Japanese, the Chinese, the Germans, the Americans, the English, the Norwegians, and many others.

Formerly the study of modern societies was left to the sociologist (sociology = the study of society). Today the methods of the cultural anthropologist have greatly influenced those of the sociologist, but the difference between the two disciplines remains: the sociologist studies modern societies in great detail; the anthropologist brings to the study of modern societies a method which is at once wider and deeper than that of the sociologist.

Today there are specialists who are known as *applied* anthropologists. These are essentially cultural anthropologists who bring their special methods to bear principally upon the problems of industry. They go into a plant and study the relationships between the workers and their employers, between the worker and his work, and they advise on the methods of improving these relationships.

There are cultural anthropologists who work in hospitals in collaboration with psychiatrists. They study the relationships within the hospital between patient and doctor, administration and staff, and they conduct collaborative studies of whole districts in order to throw light upon the genesis of mental illness and its possible prevention.

The collaboration between anthropologists and psychiatrists in the study of the cultures of different societies has been very fruitful indeed, and holds much promise for the future.

Another branch of cultural anthropology is *archaeology*

(often unkindly called the moldier part of anthropology). Archaeology is the science which studies cultures that no longer exist, basing its findings on the study of cultural products and subsistence remains recovered by excavation and similar means. If anthropologists are "the glamour boys" of the social sciences, archaeologists are "the glamour boys" of anthropology. All of which means that their specialty can be a very exciting one indeed, even though it generally entails a great deal of hard work, with far too much sand in one's hair, one's boots, and one's dried-out sandwiches. What the archaeologist is interested in doing is not merely to disinter an extinct culture, but to trace its relationships to other cultures. In this way archaeologists have been able to solve many problems which would otherwise have remained puzzling and to link up cultures which in their present form hardly seem related.

Anthropological archaeologists are to be distinguished from classical archaeologists; the latter are interested in the extinct cultures of classical antiquity, such as those of Greece, Rome, Crete, Persia, and Palestine.

Physical Anthropology

Just as the cultural anthropologist is interested in studying man as a cultural being, so the physical anthropologist is interested in the comparative study of man as a physical being. The physical anthropologist studies the origin and evolution of man's physical characters and the diversity of forms which those physical characters may take. He tries to discover the means by which the likenesses and the differences between groups of human beings have been produced. He tries to discover how man, in his various physical shapes, got to be the way he is now.

There are all sorts of specialists in physical anthropology.

There are those who study man's origin and evolution; these are called paleoanthropologists (paleo = old). They study the extinct remains of man and everything related to them. Then there are those who study the comparative anatomy of the primates, the classificatory group to which man in common with the apes and monkeys belongs. Here the primatologist, as he is called, is interested in discovering possible physical relationships between the large variety of types that constitute this group.

There are physical anthropologists who study growth and development. There are those who study physiology, and those who study the blood groups and blood types. There are those that study the so-called "races" of man, and there are a few who study all these subjects in the attempt to unify what they know into a consistent body of knowledge.

There are also applied physical anthropologists. These are largely concerned with the measurement of man, anatomically and physiologically, in order to determine, for example, standards for clothes, equipment in the armed forces, seats for railroad cars, hat sizes for men, shoe sizes for women, and the like.

There are also some constitutional physical anthropologists. These attempt to study the possible relationships between body-form and disease, body-form and personality, and even body-form and race.

Anthropology and Humanity

The anthropologist is first and foremost interested in human beings, no matter what the shape of their heads, the color of their skin, or the form of their noses. As a scientist he is interested in the facts about human beings, and as an anthropologist he knows that the facts are vastly more interesting than the fancies, the false beliefs, and the downright distortions of the facts, which some misguided persons seem always to have found it necessary to perpetrate. Humanity has a wonderfully interesting history, and it is the principal function of the anthropologist to reveal that history to the student as simply and as clearly as possible. This is what we shall now attempt to do in the following pages.

In concluding this introduction to anthropology I should like to quote the words of a great anthropologist, Thomas Henry Huxley (1825–95), writing in 1889 to a young man who later became a distinguished physical anthropologist at Cambridge University (Alfred Cort Haddon, 1855–1940). They are as true today as when they were written. Wrote Huxley: "I know of no department of natural science more likely to reward a man who goes into it thoroughly than anthropology. There is an immense deal to be done in the science pure and simple, and it is one of those branches of inquiry which brings one into contact with the great problems of humanity in every direction."

3

Man's Nearest Living Relations

Some wit once remarked that man is descended from the apes, and has been descending ever since! Both statements are untrue. It is a common belief that man is descended from "the monkeys," meaning the kinds of monkeys living today, but no scientist has ever held this belief. What, then, is the relationship of man to the monkeys and apes? Is man in any way connected with these creatures? How does one go about finding out whether he is or not?

Putting Man in His Proper Place

The best way to find out in which group any animal belongs is to ask the question: What kind of animal does our specimen most closely resemble? In our case the specimen is man. Does he resemble a fish? Not really. A cat? No. A bird? Most certainly not. A snake? Of course not. An elephant? No, no. A monkey? Well, yes, he resembles a monkey a great deal more than any of the other animals we have mentioned.

Well, what monkey does he most resemble? The fact is he most resembles an ape rather than a monkey. There are four apes: the gibbon, the orangutan, the chimpanzee, and the gorilla. Which does he most resemble? Most scientists say the gorilla. Very well, then. Man most closely resembles the gorilla of all the living creatures on this earth. He also bears striking resemblances to the monkeys. The monkeys bear striking resemblances to the little tarsiers of Malaysia, and these bear significant resemblances to the lemurs of Madagascar and the Comoro Islands.

The lemurs, tarsiers, monkeys, apes, and men seem, then, to form a common group in virtue of their physical resemblances to each other. This they do, and it was precisely for this reason that Linnaeus put them all into the same large group of animals, the Order of Primates. (An *order* is a classificatory group within a larger *class* of animals that bear certain structural relationships to each other.) "Primate" means "first in rank or order." By the name "primates," Linnaeus meant to suggest that this was the foremost or highest order of animals.

We owe the classificatory method of dealing with animals and plants to Linnaeus, who published it in his *Systema Naturae* in 1735, the 1758 edition of which serves as the basis of Linnaean nomenclature. The point and the purpose of all classification is to provide a simple practical means by which students may know what they are talking about and enable others to find out. In Table 1 you will find a classification of the primates with the subdivisions, scientific names, and popular names.

It should be noted that the names given to suborders and to superfamilies often terminate in "oidea," while the names given to families terminate in "idae," and those given to subfamilies in "inae." In the Linnaean classification the genera are given as proper names without any categorical stem end-

Sub-order	Infra-order and Series	Super-family	Family	Subfamily	Genus	Common Name
PROSIMII	LEMURIFORMES		Lemuridae	Lemurinae	Lemur Hapalemur (*Myoxicebus*) Lepilemur Mixocebus	True Lemurs Gentle Lemurs Sportive Lemurs Hattock
				Cheirogaleinae	Cheirogaleus Microcebus Opolemur (Altililemur)	Mouse Lemurs Dwarf Lemurs Fat-tailed Lemurs
	LORISIFORMES		Indriidae		Indris Propithecus Lichanotus	Endrina Sifaka Woolly Avahi
			Daubentoniidae		Daubentonia	Aye-Aye
			Galagidae	Galaginae	Galago Hemigalago	Bush Baby Lesser Bush Baby
	TARSIIFORMES		Lorisidae	Lorisinae	Loris Nycticebus Arctocebus Perodicticus	Slender Loris Slow Loris Angwantibo Potto
			Tarsiidae		Tarsius	Tarsier
ANTHROPOIDEA	PLATYRRHINI	CEBOIDEA	Callithricidae	Callithricinae	Callithrix Oedipomidas Cebuella Leontocebus	True Marmoset Crested Bare-faced Tamarin Pygmy Marmoset Lion Marmoset
			Cebidae	Callimiconinae	Callimico	Callimico
				Aotinae	Aotes Callicebus	Night Monkey Titi or Widow Monkey
				Pitheciinae	Pithecia Chiroptes Cacajao	Hairy Saki Monkey Short-haired Saki Ukari or Short-tailed Monkey
				Cebinae	Saimiri Cebus	Squirrel Monkey Capuchin Monkey
				Atelinae	Lagothrix Ateles Brachyteles	Woolly Monkey Spider Monkey Woolly Spider Monkey
				Alouattinae	Alouatta	Howler Monkey
	CATARRHINI	CERCOPITHECOIDEA	Cercopithecidae	Cercopithecinae	Cercopithecus Erythrocebus Cercocebus Macaca Cynopithecus Theropithecus Papio Mandrillus	Guenons Red-haired Patas Mangabey Macaque Celebes or Black Ape Gelada Baboon Typical Baboon Mandrill and Drill
				Semnopithecinae	Semnopithecus Colobus Rhinopithecus Nasalis	Langur Guereza Snub-nosed Langur Proboscis Monkey
		HOMINOIDEA	Hylobatidae	Hylobatinae	Hylobates Symphalangus	Common Gibbon Siamang
			Pongidae	Ponginae	Pongo Pan Gorilla	Orangutan Chimpanzee Gorilla
			Hominidae		Homo	Man

TABLE I. CLASSIFICATION OF THE PRIMATES

ing. The name of the species always follows that of the genus, and that of the subspecies follows that of the species.

The primates form a distinct and recognizable group. So far so good. But from what and where did the primates originate?

The Origin of the Primates

The creatures that most look like lemurs—the lowest members of the Primate Order—are known as insectivores or oriental tree shrews. They are to be found mostly in the Malaysian

FIG. 1   *Tree shrew* (Urogale everetti),
Philippines

Era	Period	Epoch	Millions of Years Since the Beginning of Each Epoch	Forms of Life
CENOZOIC The Age of Mammals	Quaternary	Recent	1/40	Man, the slave and master.
		Pleistocene	1	*Pithecanthropus, Sinanthropus, Swanscombe, Homo sapiens.*
	Tertiary	Pliocene	12	First men probably appeared during the latter part of this epoch, at present known only from eoliths.
		Miocene	28	Appearance of true anthropoid apes. *Dryopithecus, Sivapithecus, Proconsul.*
		Oligocene	39	Primitive anthropoid apes appear such as *Propliopithecus.*
		Eocene	58	Spread of modern mammals. Tarsiers.
		Paleocene	75	Appearance of insectivorous preprimates and earliest primates, primitive lemuroids and tarsioids.
MESOZOIC The Age of Reptiles	Secondary	Cretaceous	135	Rise of archaic mammals and birds. Extinction of dinosaurs, pterodactyls, and toothed birds. Insectivores.
		Jurassic	165	Spread of primitive mammals and pterodactyls, rise of toothed birds.
		Triassic	205	Rise of dinosaurs, pterodactyls, and primitive mammals.
PALEOZOIC The Age of Ancient Life		Permian	230	Spread of amphibians and insects. Extinction of trilobites.
		Carboniferous	255	Primitive reptiles, insects, spiders. Great forests of ferns and mosses.
		Devonian	325	Rise of fishes and amphibians. Spreading of forests.
		Silurian	360	Rise of ostracoderms, sea-scorpions (Eurypterids). First land plants.
		Ordovician	425	First primitive fishes, the ostracoderms.
		Cambrian	505	Still no land-life known, trilobites, mollusks, brachiopods.
PROTEROZOIC			925	Sponges, protozoons, diatoms, and protophyta, and other commencing complex forms of life developed during this era.
ARCHEOZOIC			1,500	Probably simple unicellular sea-dwelling forms

TABLE 2. GEOLOGICAL TIME-SCALE OF THE APPEARANCE OF VARIOUS REPRESENTATIVE FORMS OF LIFE

The estimated number of millions of years in the fourth column for the Tertiary period is based upon a combination of paleontological data, with specific reference to the evolution of the horse from *Hyracotherium* to *Equus,* and the evidence of geology and radiocativity. The figures for the preceding periods are largely based on the uranium transformation method. When uranium and lead occur together in a fragment of rock otherwise free from these elements, it may generally be safely assumed that the lead represents "decomposed" or transformed uranium. It is known that 1,000,000 grams of uranium yields 1/7600 grams of lead a year. Hence the age of such rocks can be determined from the proportions of these elements which they contain, thus:

$$\text{Age of rock} = \frac{\text{Weight of Lead}}{\text{Weight of Uranium}} \times 7600 \text{ million years}$$

region, and also in China and India. The group of tree shrews that look most like the lemurs are known as tupaias. The tupaia looks something like a long-snouted mouse, and is actually not much bigger. The earliest tupaias or insectivores are known from the Cretaceous geological epoch, which goes back to more than 75 million years ago. That's when we think the first primates came into being, somewhere in the late Cretaceous or the early Paleocene epoch. (Look at, and try to memorize, Table 2, which lists the geological eras, periods, and epochs and the forms of life typically associated with them.) Most experts today feel that the tupaias should be classed with the primates.

The early insectivorous primates, as their name implies, were chiefly insect-eaters. They lived mostly in the lower branches of bushes and trees. Their brains were largely smell brains. Since these early primates earned their living by keeping their noses to the ground, as it were, by smelling out their food, their brains would have to be largely organized along smell lines. Their eyes were situated on each side of the face rather than in front (as in ourselves), and their tails helped them to balance themselves on the limbs of trees. Tupaias are nocturnal animals, that is, they go to sleep during the daylight hours and are wakeful only during the night hours. The probable reason for this we shall get around to seeing later.

The Lemurs: Family Lemuridae

The lemurs are foxlike creatures that vary in size from the size of a mouse to an average-sized dog. The small lemurs are nocturnal, the large ones diurnal (awake during daylight and asleep at night). They have nonprehensile (prehensile = grasping) tails which they use for balancing, and the eyes tend to be more toward the front of the face than in the tupaias.

They seem to divide their time between a life on the ground and a life in the trees. The smell part of the brain is somewhat smaller in size, while the back part of the brain associated with vision is more highly developed than in the tupaias. The brain

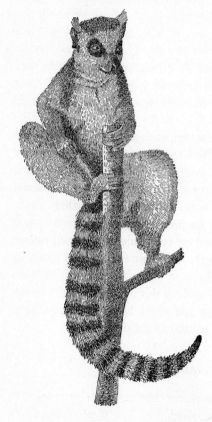

FIG. 2   *Ring-tailed lemur*
(Lemur catta)
Madagascar

is, however, still to a significant extent a smell brain, and in the parts of the world where lemurs live, Madagascar, Malaysia, Africa, Ceylon, and southern India, one may see lemurs of various shapes and forms still mostly relying upon the sense of smell in order to gain a living. The lemurs seem to have gone on a merry spree of specializing in many different forms, and while they have managed to exist for a very long time, they don't seem to have given rise to any higher forms.

The Tarsiers: Genus Tarsius

The tarsiers live in the Malay Archipelago and the Philippines. They are about eight inches long, with long, tufted tails, flat faces, and the most enormous eyes set in the front of their faces of any of the primates. This animal is called spectral tarsier, "spectral" because of its large eyes and "tarsier" because of the greatly elongated tarsal bones in each foot. (The heel bone, or calcaneus, and the navicular at its side together form part of the tarsus.) The tarsier is nocturnal, and spends most of his time in the trees. *Tarsius spectrum* possesses the peculiar capacity of being able to swivel his head around an orbit which completes 180 degrees so that his nose is in line with his spinal column, a feat which has been celebrated in the limerick:

> *The Tarsier, weird little beast*
> *Can't swivel his eyes in the least,*
> *But when sitting at rest*
> *With his tummy due west*
> *He can screw his head round to face east.*

A very interesting thing about the tarsiers is exhibited in the smallness of the smell parts of the brain as compared with the same parts in the lemurs. In correlation with this the snout shows reduction, but the eyes have enlarged. Notice this association, because it is most significant. Tarsiers are really arboreal creatures, that is to say, they are adapted for living in trees. A monkey in the trees has to earn its living in a way quite different from one who lives on the ground. On the ground the animal needs its sense of smell most. In the trees the sense of smell isn't of much help; what the animal needs most is vision, good vision. In order to catch flies and other insects, it must be able to follow their movements and those of any other small creatures that may be wandering around in the trees. And in the trees it also needs to free its forelimbs so

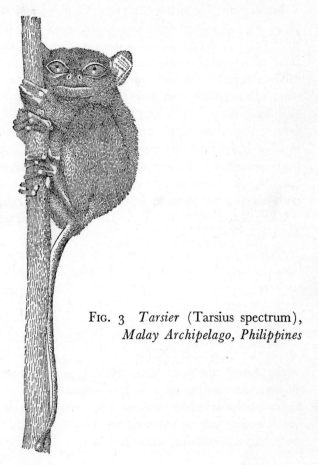

FIG. 3   *Tarsier* (Tarsius spectrum), *Malay Archipelago, Philippines*

that it can catch and deal with these creatures with its hands. This the tarsiers have done. They have well-developed hands with opposable thumbs, that is, thumbs that can turn on their own axis to face the palmar surface of the fingers. *Tarsius*, altogether, is quite a character.

Most authorities believe that from the tarsiers the monkeys and apes arose. The first tarsiers are found in the Eocene epoch of North America, and because the earliest tarsioids (tarsius-like creatures) and lemuroids are found in North America, it is this country which is believed to be the birthplace of the primates.

The tarsiers are important for us to study because they show the beginning development of what probably constitutes the most important single factor in the evolution of the primates, namely, the increasing importance and dominance of the sense of vision and the correlated changes associated with it. This vastly increased what has been called "the space of recognition." In other words, it greatly enlarged the possibilities of experience for the primates.

Like most of the other nocturnal primates, *Tarsius* lives in small family groups rather than in large communities, though there is, of course, some sort of cross-communication between families or members of families within the larger population of tarsiers.

The South American Monkeys or New World Monkeys: Families Callithricidae and Cebidae

The South American monkeys range in size from the tiny marmosets to the *Ateles* monkeys (who have no thumbs but highly prehensile tails) which reach a height of almost three feet. The durukulis or night monkeys of Nicaragua, Peru, and the Amazon constitute good links between the tarsiers and the monkeys, for the durukulis are nocturnal, small in size, and live in small family groups. Otherwise they are much more like monkeys than they are like tarsiers.

All South American monkeys are arboreal, but only half of

FIG. 4 *Spider monkey* (Ateles ater), *Mexico to Amazon basin*

the genera own prehensile tails, and most of them don't have opposable thumbs. What they lack in opposability of thumbs many of them make up with prehensility of tails. The *Ateles* or spider monkeys can actually use their tails as a sort of third hand, being able to pick up all sorts of things with it.

The brain of the South American monkey is pre-eminently a seeing one, with the functions and structures subserving the sense of smell very considerably reduced. There is no doubt that the South American monkeys gave rise to the Old World or Eastern Hemisphere monkeys.

The Eastern Hemisphere Monkeys or Old World Monkeys: Family Cercopithecidae

All the Old World monkeys are Asiatic and African in distribution (with the exception of the Barbary ape which was introduced to the Rock of Gibraltar in Europe more than a century ago). The Old World monkeys are very like their New World cousins except that they do not have prehensile tails, their thumbs are opposable, and they have only two premolar or bicuspid teeth (the teeth immediately after the eye or canine teeth) on each side of the jaw instead of the three that the New World monkeys have. There are all sorts of Old World monkeys, some of them reaching the size of big dogs, such as the baboons, those highly colored creatures with scarlet and blue faces and often equally garishly colored seats. Not all baboons are so flamboyantly decorated, only, it appears, the most doggish of them.

The brains of the Old World monkeys are distinctly seeing ones; smell is poorly developed, and intelligence doesn't seem to be any higher in them than it is in the New World monkeys. In fact, there is a most remarkable identity in form and appearance of the brain in the two great groups of monkeys. This probably represents the persistence, over the course of some 50 million years, of a complex trait that was, and still is, characteristic of the original New World monkeys, and which has endured over this immensely long period of time in the Old World monkeys.

The Old World monkeys undoubtedly gave rise to some apes, all of which became extinct long ago. Many of these are known from their fossil remains, enabling us to reconstruct something of the evolution of the primates. The early tarsiers

FIG. 5   *Barbary ape* (Macaca sylvana), *Gibraltar, Asia, Malaysia, Africa*

may very well have been the ancestors of early intermediate forms before the apes finally arose from these. The intermediate forms were either very like Old World monkeys or identical with them.

The Apes: Families Hylobatidae and Pongidae

The apes consist of the gibbon, orangutan, chimpanzee, and gorilla.

The gibbon (genus *Hylobates*) is the acrobat among the primates, for he has developed the most amazing agility in the trees. Here he can negotiate his way faster than a man can run on the ground. When he stands erect, his fingers touch the ground, so long are his upper extremities. He is an inhabitant mainly of Asia. Another form of gibbon, the siamang (genus *Symphalangus*) is found on the island of Sumatra. Ever since the Oligocene epoch, some 39 million years ago, the gibbons seem to have pursued their independent evolution, quite apart from any of the other apes. Fossil forms of the gibbon from that epoch indicate that there has not actually been much change over this long period of time. The gibbons rarely reach three feet in height. They have a small brain capacity, about 100 cubic centimeters (c.c.), but a highly developed visual one. They certainly stand a long way off from the direct line of man's ancestry.

The orangutan (Malay for "wild-man-of-the-woods"; genus *Pongo*) is a delightful creature who lives exclusively in Borneo and Sumatra. He is entirely arboreal, with shaggy, reddish-brown hair and a face that is often pathetically manlike. He has a good-sized brain (about 400 c.c.) with intelligence to match, and is reputedly the strongest creature in the jungle. Orangs have been known, when attacked, to pull the jaws of giant crocodiles apart and then fling the victim into the water as if it were a broken reed. Yet the male orang weighs no more than 165 pounds, while the female rarely weighs more than 80 pounds.

More manlike than the orangutan is the chimpanzee (genus

Pan). The chimpanzee is an inhabitant of western and eastern equatorial Africa. The male weighs about 110 pounds and the female about 88 pounds. The average height of the male is five feet and of the female four feet. Chimpanzees are expert tree climbers, but they spend much time on the ground. They have a brain capacity of about 400 c.c. They are quite intelli-

FIG. 6   *Chimpanzee* (Pan satyrus), *western and central Equatorial Africa*

gent creatures and as everyone knows, can be taught many tricks requiring great control and intelligence.

Chimpanzees do not have a bridge, or raised bones, to their noses, their jaws are rather projecting, and they have quite well-developed canine teeth. Like the orang they are vegetarian, and among themselves and with all other creatures are thoroughly peaceful.

It should be remembered that when any of the apes, or any other animals, are seen in a zoo, they are in the most unnatural of conditions. Quite frequently they are isolated from their kind, but even when this is not so, they are usually most unhappy and only too frequently mentally ill—just as we would be if we were treated, or rather mistreated, in a similar manner. Under conditions of confinement, the chimpanzee seems to become manic and hyperactive, whereas the gorilla grows depressed and despondent.

The chimpanzee does not walk erect, although he can do so when he desires; his habitual mode of progression is in an obliquely quadrupedal position with the knuckles of his digits bent to support him in front. He has a short opposable thumb, between which and his forefinger he can hold and thread a needle with the best of needleworkers.

Dr. Ludwig Heck, the head of the Zoological Gardens in Berlin, who has had much experience with chimpanzees, considers that they are kind and generous by nature, and he describes how they will give away part of their own food to a hungry companion and go to one another's aid when such help is needed. One of his chimpanzees succeeded in pulling a splinter out of a keeper's hand, and made a very neat job of it, too.

All authorities are agreed that the modern chimpanzee does not stand in the direct line of man's ancestry. The chimpanzee, in common with the orang and gorilla, probably originated during the Miocene epoch some 28 million years ago, or at least their immediate ancestors did. We have the fossil remains of chimpanzeelike creatures known as the subfamily Dryopithecinae or the genus *Dryopithecus* from India and from Europe.

Ever since the Miocene epoch the chimpanzee and the gorilla (and the orang) have been pursuing their own evolutionary destiny quite apart from man.

The Gorilla: Genus Gorilla

The gorilla lives in east-central and western equatorial Africa. There are two kinds of gorilla, which differ very slightly from one another, the lowland or coastal gorilla of East Africa, known as *Gorilla gorilla gorilla* (yes, three times, giving the genus, species, and subspecies or race), and the West African highland or mountain gorilla, *Gorilla gorilla beringei* (after Captain von Beringe, a German officer who first described it).

The gorilla is the bulkiest of the primates. Gorillas are not as tall as most people imagine, being on the average only about five and a half feet. Weights up to 670 pounds have been recorded. As in the other apes, the forelimbs are longer than the hind limbs. Undoubtedly the gorilla is the strongest of all primates. Gorillas have bare chests, not hairy ones as is commonly believed. Otherwise, they are covered with black hair except on the face. Some of the hairs on the top of the head may be variously colored. While the orang can grow a beard and mustache, the chimpanzee and gorilla cannot.

The average male cranial or brain capacity is 550 c.c., while that of the female is about 460 c.c. The face is most interesting because the nasal bones show a slight elevation, so that the nose, while still quite flattish, is more like that of man than the nose of any of the other apes. The lips, as in all the apes,

FIG. 7 *Male gorilla (believed to be* Gorilla gorilla beringei, *the mountain gorilla), western and eastern Equatorial Africa*

are very thin with hardly any of the reddish-looking mucous membrane furled outward as in ourselves.

Gorillas are terrestrial creatures, that is, they live on the ground. But they are good tree climbers. They build nests, mostly on the ground, in which to sleep and never use these more than once. Their diet is principally herbivorous, that is, they feed chiefly on plants. Gorillas usually live in small bands of from three to ten or more families. During the day they generally separate but return before or at nightfall to make their nests together. All the apes are peaceful animals, and they will never attack any living thing unless seriously provoked or badly frightened.

The gorilla moves about in much the same way as the chimpanzee, in an obliquely quadrupedal position, and like the chimpanzee the gorilla can move, when it wants to, in the erect position.

The Apes Summarized

All apes are without tails whereas all monkeys have tails. All apes have both opposable thumbs and big toes, and all of them have flattened nails on their fingers and toes. Some of the lower monkeys have claws. The great apes (this excludes the gibbon) are all over four feet in height, have largish brains, and are the most intelligent of the nonhuman primates. They are all diurnal in their habits, mostly vegetarian, and live in small family bands. They all have large canine teeth, very unlike those of men, and are covered with an abundant growth of body hair. The face of the gorilla is always black, but the chimpanzee will vary all the way from white to mottled brown and black. The orang may be white-skinned or mottled-brown. The gibbon is usually black-skinned, though his body hair may vary from white to black.

In structure the apes living today are far too different from men to be in the direct line of their ancestry. They are at most remote collateral relatives or distant "cousins" of ours. Today's apes are too specialized to be ancestors of ours, that is to say, they have developed all sorts of special traits, like large eye (canine) teeth, and in the case of the gorilla great bulk. The immediate nonhuman ancestors of man must have been very much less apelike than the great apes.

Let us see in the next chapter what is known of the possible ancestors of man.

4

The Ancestry of Man

IN SOUTH AFRICA, especially since the late twenties, there
have been unearthed a large number of skeletons of fossil
apes, which have been named the australopithecines (*australis*
= south, *pithecus* = ape). The remarkable thing about the
australopithecines is that they are in every respect apelike, except that their brain capacity is larger and that their hipbones
and the bones of the thigh (femur), leg (tibia and fibula),
and foot are manlike.

From the structure of the hip and leg bones, it is quite evident that the australopithecines walked either erect or almost
erect. So now, for the first time, we have clear evidence of the
order of the functional evolution of some of the parts of the
human body. The erect posture was attained before the brain
evolved to a near-human status. Some authorities used to think
that it might have been the other way around. Now we know
for certain that man's ancestors stood erect first, before their
brains changed toward human status.

How long ago did the australopithecines live? We don't know with certainty because the geology (the study of the earth) of the regions of South Africa in which the australopithecine remains are found is not well understood. But most authorities are of the opinion that these fossil remains date back to the Lower Pleistocene, that is to say, about a million or more years ago. They may have died out in South Africa about a quarter of a million years ago or even later, but that doesn't mean that they could not have been ancestral to man or closely related to the group of ancient apes which were the direct ancestors of man.

Man's Ancestors—Are They the Australopithecines?

The australopithecines had an average brain size of less than 600 c.c.; the average brain size of living men today is about 1350 c.c. The australopithecines would therefore have had quite a long way to go before they reached the status of man; they would have had to add approximately an additional 400 c.c. to their brain capacity to reach the status of the earliest man, *Pithecanthropus erectus*. A rapid jump of 400 c.c. is inconceivable.

Furthermore, the skull form of all australopithecines is extremely apelike. The vault of the skull is low, and in some forms like *Paranthropus crassidens*, there is a well-developed crest, similar to that of the male gorilla, which runs from back to front on the top of the head. (This sagittal crest, as it is called, serves for the attachment of the massive muscles at the sides of the head which move the lower jaw up and down.) In others, such as *Paranthropus robustus*, the lower jaw is of massive thickness. These are obviously special developments away from the direction which led to the line of man. Such creatures could not have been directly ancestral to man. But the fact is that the australopithecines do exhibit many man-like characters. The teeth, for example, are more like those of human beings than those of any other known creature. So are the bones of the lower extremity and the hip.

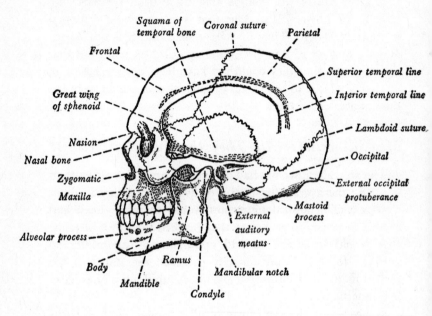

FIG. 8   *Human skull*

Putting such facts together, most authorities have concluded that the australopithecines show too many specialized and apelike characters to be either the direct ancestors of man or of the line that led to man, but that owing to their possession of many manlike characters they are probably closely related to the group which actually gave rise to man. We have no knowledge of man's actual apelike ancestors from the discovery of their remains, but we do have some idea of what

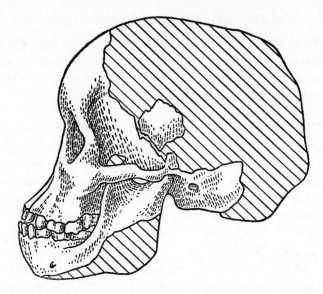

FIG. 9 *Skull of* Australopithecus africanus *(right side reversed). The diagonally shaded areas are reconstructed*

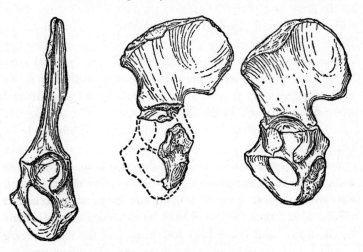

FIG. 10 *Left side views of pelvic bones in chimpanzee (left),* Australopithecus prometheus *(center), and Bushman (right)*

they will look like when they are, as we believe they will be, found.

Man's Probable Ancestors

Man's ancestors will probably be found to have been rather unspecialized creatures possessing a great many primitive characters, creatures that looked very much more like men than they did like apes. Such creatures would have preserved a strong tendency not to develop tusklike eye teeth, great weight, sagittal crests, or other such specializations, but would have maintained a somewhat conservative tendency to enlarge on the endowments they already possessed. For example, the tendency in the evolution of the primates has been for brain size to increase. Any animal group concentrating, metaphorically speaking, upon increase in brain size, rather than upon developing a massive skull with all sorts of excrescences on it, would in the long run stand a good chance of throwing up those traits which would lead to the achievement of human status. But this is, of course, only a way of speaking. No creature has ever concentrated on the development of any physical trait (with the exception of man). What we really intend to say is that creatures that are forced to use their brains a great deal in adapting to their environment are more likely to take advantage of any variations in improved brains that happen to be born among them.

Such creatures would first have developed the upright posture, as we know the australopithecines to have done. Second, they would never have developed the large, overspecialized canine tooth; thus they would not have needed so much bone in the upper and lower jaws for them, and the snout region would have been reduced in the direction of the rather straight-facedness of man. Third, the brain would have been enlarged, with corresponding changes in the form of the skull, in the direction of a more domelike top of the head and the development of a forehead. Rearrangement of the facial bones and the rendering more vertical of the front of the head would produce an elevation and forward projection of the nasal bones—which in the monkeys remain flat—culminating in the unique structure which we know as the nose of man.

It is quite probable that man's immediate ancestors as a group had already lost a considerable part of the hairy coat

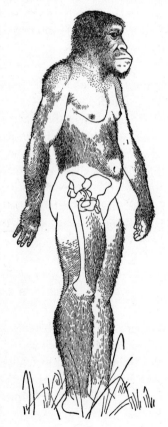

FIG. 11 *Reconstruction of a typical australopithecine*

which is characteristic of all anthropoids, indeed, of all primates. What the skin color was we cannot be sure, but since the ancestors of man were almost certainly tropical animals of African origin, they were almost equally certainly black-skinned.

Did they have speech? We don't know. Perhaps they had the rudiments. Did they have tools? It is quite possible that they did. In certain parts of South Africa a peculiar kind of small, flaked pebble is found in great numbers, which evidently served as a tool. These may well have been made by a group ancestral to man. Some have been found together with the teeth of australopithecines. It has been alleged that the australopithecines used the limb bones of baboons as implements. The fact that many baboon skulls have been found associated with australopithecine remains, in such condition as to suggest that they were bashed in from the top, has led Professor Raymond Dart of South Africa to infer that this was the handiwork of australopithecines and that the latter must have used tools or implements. Most authorities on this matter tend to maintain a reasonable doubt in the absence of further evidence.

The search for "the missing link" has not yet been completed. We may be sure that it will not be long before that missing link is discovered.

The Most Primitive Men: Gigantopithecus blacki and Meganthropus palaeojavanicus

The most primitive types of men, the types of men who stand nearest the apes and are yet men, have been found in the Sino-Malayan region, specifically in Java and in China.

In China it has been an age-old custom to dig up so-called "dragon bones," which are, of course, the fossil bones of many different kinds of animals, and sell these, either whole or ground up, to the apothecary shops as a potent medicine for practically every disease. It may seem strange that a geologist should consider it part of his job to explore the contents of Chinese apothecary shops in search of fossil material, but when we learn that it was by so doing that the Dutch geologist G. H. R. von Koenigswald discovered the tooth of one of the most primitive manlike forms known to scientists, it will not seem so strange after all. Actually Dr. von Koenigswald discovered three manlike molar teeth. These consisted of right and left lower third molars belonging to different individuals, and an upper molar probably belonging to still a third individual. The striking thing about these teeth is their size. They are enormous. The volume of the crown of the lower third molar is about six times larger than that of the equivalent tooth in modern man, and it is almost twice as large as the corresponding tooth of the gorilla.

This creature should properly be called *Gigantanthropus* (giant man), but the rules of systematics, in the form of the law of priority, render it obligatory to continue to use the first name bestowed upon the specimen, *Gigantopithecus blacki* (giant ape, *blacki* in honor of Davidson Black, who had discovered *Sinanthropus*).

In fact the creatures to which these teeth belonged were tremendously robust ape-men. It is thought, by many authorities, that the gigantopithecines may well be closely related to some of the rather massively built types of australopithecines. The geological horizon of *Gigantopithecus* is probably the Middle Pleistocene.

Perhaps the oldest type of manlike form known (*Meganthropus palaeojavanicus*) was discovered in 1941 by Dr. von Koenigswald in the form of the fragments of two lower jaws in the Lower Pleistocene beds of the Sangiran district in central Java. These jaws are extraordinarily massive, achieving the proportions of the jaw of an adult male gorilla. Nevertheless, the form of the jaw is distinctly human.

Pithecanthropus erectus

During the years 1890–97 a young Dutch physician named Eugene Dubois, who had gone out to Java in search of "the missing link," discovered at Trinil in central Java, the top of

FIG. 12   *Skull of* Pithecanthropus erectus

a skull, a thigh bone, the fragment of a lower jaw, and three teeth. These were all strikingly manlike, though the skullcap still looked pretty primitive. The thigh bone was almost like that of a modern man, suggesting that the creature to which it belonged had walked erect. This combination of apelike top of the head and manlike thigh bone, suggested the name "the ape-man who walked erect," hence, in its Latin form, *Pithecanthropus erectus.*

The brain capacity of *Pithecanthropus erectus* has been computed to be between 860 and 940 c.c. This is actually within the range of modern man. Modern European men with a brain capacity of 875 c.c. with good intelligence have been recorded; in fact, the great French writer Anatole France had a brain capacity of slightly over 1000 c.c.

It was not until many years later that Dr. von Koenigswald, in 1937, discovered several other specimens of *Pithecanthropus erectus* in the Sangiran district of central Java. All *Pithecanthropus erectus* remains are from the Middle Pleistocene epoch.

Pithecanthropus robustus

One of the most important of Dr. von Koenigswald's finds, in 1939, was that of a very robust form of *Pithecanthropus,* therefore called *Pithecanthropus robustus.* This consisted of the back and the base of the skull and the upper jaw with the teeth in their sockets. The teeth are essentially human in form, except that the canines project beyond the level of the other teeth, and there is a bony space between the canine and the lateral incisor for the reception of the tip of the lower canine, just as in the apes. In *Pithecanthropus erectus* this space has disappeared.

The evidence, therefore, points to this evolutionary order of changes in the jaw region, namely, that first the canine tooth underwent reduction, as we can see in *Pithecanthropus robustus,* and that this was followed after a time by disappearance of the premaxillary diastema, as the space between the canine tooth and the lateral incisor is called. In this way the projection of the upper jaw was reduced to the more or less straight form characteristic of modern man.

Solo Man

Near Ngandong in central Java in 1931, in the region of the Solo River, there were found eleven fossil skulls. Faces and teeth were missing, but the skulls, which were extraordinarily thick, showed distinct resemblances to *Pithecanthropus* on the one hand and to the later forms of man known as Neanderthal on the other. The average brain capacity was 1100 c.c.

With the remains of Solo man were found examples of his handiwork in the form of several beautifully worked bone implements, an ax made of deer antlers, a barbed spearhead, and a number of somewhat crudely fashioned stones. Solo man appears, then, to have been quite an advanced form culturally, belonging somewhere in the Upper Paleolithic or Upper Old Stone Age (see Table 4).

Direct association of such implements with *Pithecanthropus* has never been demonstrated, but throughout the Sino-Malayan region there are found a variety of chopping tools which may have been the handiwork of the pithecanthropines.

Sinanthropus pekinensis

Sinanthropus pekinensis means Chinese man from Peking. This name was given to a new form of man by Professor Davidson Black, then of Peking Union Medical College, on the basis of the discovery of a single tooth at Chouk'outien, just about thirty-seven miles southwest of Peking. This was in 1927. By 1939 the remains of over forty individuals had been recovered, and new digging begun in 1943 on the original Middle Pleistocene site has succeeded in uncovering the remains of additional skeletal parts.

Unfortunately the original skeletal remains of *Sinanthropus* were lost while they were being transported to an unachieved safety during the Japanese invasion of China. Casts, however, of most of the original material are available as well as good photographs and drawings.

The average brain capacity of *Sinanthropus* is 1075 c.c. Brain size is about 20 per cent greater than that of *Pithecan-*

thropus. The forehead region is slightly more developed in *Sinanthropus* than in *Pithecanthropus*. The teeth are human in form, and there is no space between the canine tooth and the

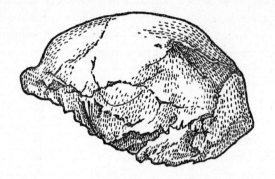

FIG. 13 *Skull of* Sinanthropus
pekinensis

lateral incisor in the upper jaw, but, as in the pithecanthropines, a chin is lacking.

Many tools of the chopper and cutting types were found associated with *Sinanthropus*.

It has been asserted that *Sinanthropus* was a cannibal since the bases of all the skulls were found broken open, and many of the long bones had been split longitudinally by some human means. The suggestion is that *Sinanthropus* extracted the brain and ate it, and also sucked on the long bones to extract the marrow. This is possible, but unproven. Most human beings are capable of cannibalism under conditions of extreme starvation.

The resemblances between *Pithecanthropus* and *Sinanthropus* are very striking, and all in all it seems justifiable to conclude that the latter represents a slightly more advanced geographic variety of the former and can be included in the term "pithecanthropine."

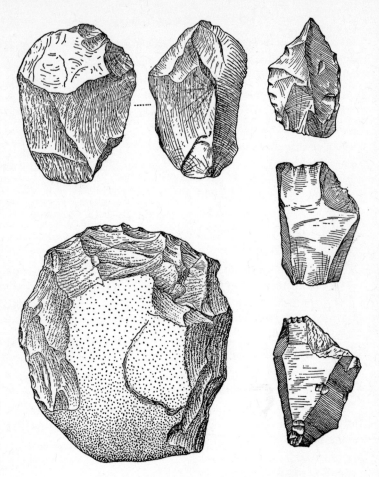

FIG. 14 *Stone tools of Pekin man*

Atlanthropus mauritanicus

In June, 1954, Professor C. Arambourg of the National Museum of Natural History at Paris discovered two human lower jaws in a pit at Ternifine in Algeria. These jaws came from a Lower Middle Pleistocene (Kamasian industry) horizon, to which Professor Arambourg attributes an age of about half a million years. The jaws, which are very robustly built, are chinless and strongly resemble those of the pithecanthropines, *Pithecanthropus* and *Sinanthropus*, but are sufficiently different from them to warrant identifying them as a new form of fossil man, *Atlanthropus mauritanicus*.

The teeth in *Atlanthropus* are unmistakably human and most closely resemble those of the pithecanthropines. Associated with these jaws were found the remains of many extinct animals and numerous roughly worked stone tools of quartzite, limestone, and flint, representatives of the most ancient type of workmanship (Abbevillian-Acheulian).

A portion of a human lower jaw also found in 1954, in a Middle Pleistocene deposit at Sidi Abderrahman near Casablanca in Morocco, associated with stone tools of a Middle Acheulian industry, appears to belong to the same type as *Atlanthropus*. Thus, for the first time we have definite evidence of the presence of pithecanthropine types in Africa. Earlier, in 1934, the fragments of three skulls discovered in an Upper Paleolithic deposit northwest of Lake Eyassi, in East Africa, were by some authorities thought to be of pithecanthropine type. The type represented by these skull fragments was named *Africanthropus*. The new discoveries in North Africa greatly strengthen the claim of *Africanthropus* to pithecanthropine status.

Wadjak Man

A very interesting discovery was made by Dubois at Wadjak, some sixty miles southeast of Trinil in central Java, of two human skulls during the years 1889 and 1890. Nevertheless, the announcement of the discovery of these skulls was not made by Dubois until 1920! Dubois claimed a Pleistocene age for these two skulls, the brain capacity of one being 1550 cubic centimeters and of the other 1650 cubic centimeters.

What is so interesting about these skulls is that they bear a remarkable resemblance to the skull of the typical Australian aboriginal of today, except that they have a much larger brain capacity than the latter. It is quite possible that some members of the Wadjak population reached Australia in Pleistocene times. It has been suggested that we now have an almost continuous evolutionary line leading from *Pithecanthropus* through Solo man to Wadjak man, and thence to the Australian aboriginal.

Rhodesian Man

A complete skull minus a lower jaw of a primitive type of man was found in a cave at Broken Hill, in Northern Rhodesia, in 1921. Combining pithecanthropoid traits with modern manlike traits, Rhodesian man had a brain capacity of 1300 c.c., enormous brow ridges, a projecting, large, gorilla-like upper jaw, and an unusually broad palate. The teeth closely resemble those of contemporary man, and an interesting thing about them is that they were all badly decayed, proving that bad teeth are not a modern development. The presence of Solo-like, Neanderthal-like, and modern man-like traits combine to render the Rhodesian skull of great interest. It suggests that Rhodesian man may actually be an evolutionary product of the admixture, among other things, of such types.

In 1953 another skull of Rhodesian man, together with associated artifacts (objects made by man), was found about fifteen miles from Saldanha Bay, some sixty miles north of Cape Town in South Africa, some fifteen hundred miles from Broken Hill where the first skull was found. This proves that Rhodesian man roamed pretty widely over Africa.

Only the base and face and lower jaw are missing from the skull, but the skullcap with its sides, back, and great brow ridges quite conclusively shows that we are here dealing with the same Solo-Neanderthal-modernlike medley of traits that characterized Rhodesian man I.

In Rhodesian man, then, we have perhaps a link between Solo man of Java, Neanderthal man of many parts of the world, and the modern, or neanthropic, type of man, as he is sometimes called.

Heidelberg Man

In a quarry at Mauer, some six miles southeast of Heidelberg, Germany, the massive lower jaw of a primitive type of man, with all the teeth in place, was uncovered by a workman in 1907. This jaw is of Lower Pleistocene age. This makes Heidelberg man one of the oldest authenticated human fossils known to us.

The teeth are slightly larger than those of the average man of today but well within modern man's normal range of variation. The side of the jaw (the ramus) is very broad, and there is no chin. Heidelberg man may be a forerunner of Neanderthal man and a relative of Solo man.

Neanderthal Man

Almost everyone has heard of Neanderthal man. This type of man is now known from specimens of well over one hundred individuals, and we now know that there were many different varieties of the Neanderthal form of man. Neanderthal man is an Upper Pleistocene type.

The first thing of interest to say about Neanderthal man is that his brain was on the average larger than that of modern men. The average Neanderthal brain capacity was 1450 c.c., while that of contemporary man is less than 1400 c.c. Since Neanderthal man flourished from about 150,000 years ago or more and ceased to flourish as a type about 50,000 years ago, we must assume that the smaller size of the modern human brain is the result of an evolutionary trend or that the large brain of Neanderthal man was a trait peculiar to this type. From the evidence of some other early types of men, we have reason to believe that the human brain has actually decreased in gross size and stabilized itself about 50,000 years ago at its present size. In spite of writers in Sunday magazine supplements, it is highly unlikely that the human brain will evolve by growing larger. It doesn't have to. It can increase in complexity without increasing in size.

Neanderthal man tended to have a somewhat sloping forehead, with well-developed brow ridges, a heavy chinless jaw, and a rather projecting back of the head (occiput). Owing to the want of a little knowledge of elementary anatomy, some of those "authorities" who have engaged in the "reconstruction" of Neanderthal man have represented him with a bull neck, grotesque features, and walking with a stoop, during which, it was alleged, his knees knocked together! It has also often been asserted that Neanderthal man must have been of low intelligence because he had a low forehead. All these slanders are indefensible. Neanderthal man walked as erect as any modern man, he did not have a bull neck, and he was not knock-kneed. And it has long ago been proven by many independent scientific investigators that the form of the brow or of the head has nothing whatever to do with intelligence. As a matter of fact, we have very good reason to believe that Neanderthal man was every bit as intelligent as we are today. He made the beautiful tools which are described as belonging to the Mousterian culture (after Le Moustier in southern France where they were first found). He made flint balls, perforators, discs, scrapers, and stone knives, and he introduced the use of mineral pigments into human culture. Neanderthal man also

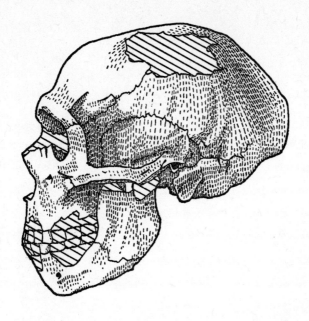

FIG. 15 *Skull of Neanderthal man, the Old Man
of La Chapelle-aux-Saints. The diagonally shaded
areas are reconstructed*

introduced ceremonial interment of the dead, thus suggesting
that he possessed a highly developed religious system.

For a long time it was believed that Neanderthal man was
exterminated by men of our own type. There was absolutely no
evidence for this belief except the kind of thinking that characterized nineteenth-century scholars of all varieties, namely,
that warfare was as old as man and was the means by which
one race conquered and exterminated another. Since Neanderthal remains are known from almost every part of the earth
where human fossils have been found, it is inconceivable that
Neanderthal man should everywhere have been exterminated.

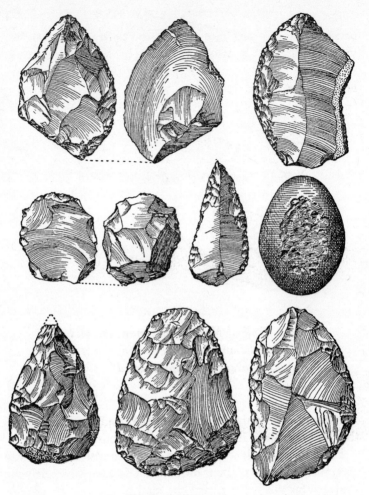

FIG. 16 *Tools of Mousterian industries*

It is doubtful whether he was exterminated anywhere. The truth seems to be that he mixed with whatever populations he encountered and in the course of time was absorbed by such populations. Certainly in Europe this was the case, for many

persons of European descent still bear the traces of their remote Neanderthal ancestry. These traces may be seen in the
rather heavy brow ridges, deep-sunk sockets, receding fore-
heads, and weakly developed chin regions.

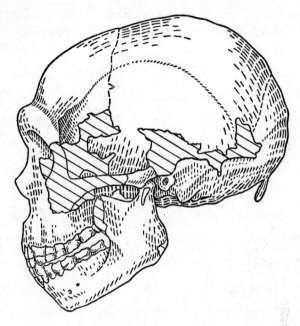

FIG. 17A *Tabūn I. Skull of Neanderthal type
from Mount Carmel, Palestine. The diagonally
shaded areas are reconstructed*

Early Mixtures of Different Types of Men

While the populations of early man were very small, there is
good reason to believe that whenever such populations met
they did exactly what modern populations do, they interbred.

Actual evidence of such intermixture was until recently a matter of speculation, but during 1931–32 the evidence became factual. For it was during this period that an assemblage of fossil neanderthaloids were discovered in caves on the slopes of Mount Carmel in Palestine.

Here were found two types, a clearly Neanderthal type, in the caves of Tabūn, and another type which closely ap-

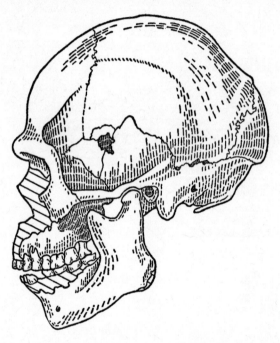

FIG. 17B   *Skūhl V (right side reversed). Skull of a mixed type, Neanderthal and the modern type of man*

proached modern man, from the caves of Skūhl. Between the two types there was every variety of intergradation. It is quite clear that there had been an intermixture between a modern-like form of man and Neanderthal men, and that the Mount Carmel population was the product of this intermixture.

There is every reason to believe that similar intermixtures occurred between early human populations throughout the long history of man.

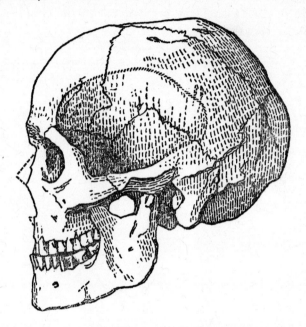

FIG. 18   *Skull of Cro-Magnon male*

Cro-Magnon Man

The Cro-Magnons are the Apollos of the prehistoric world. This form was discovered originally in 1868 in the little village of Les Eyzies in southern central France, in a rock shelter called Cro-Magnon. The remains of thirteen other individuals were uncovered between 1872 and 1902 in the caves of the Red Rocks of the Côte d'Azur, some forty minutes walk from Mentone on the Italian Riviera. A headless, incomplete skeleton found in Paviland Cave in southwestern

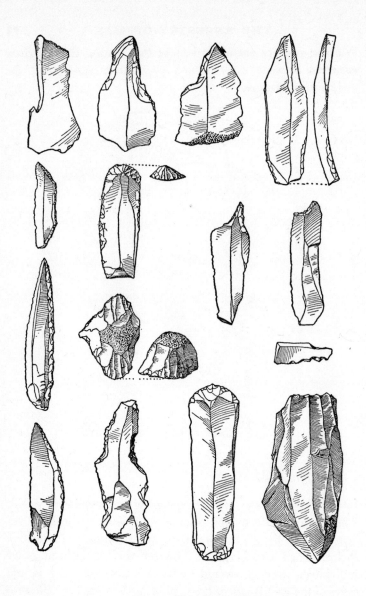

FIG. 19 *Upper Paleolithic flint tools*

Wales in 1823 almost certainly belongs to the Cro-Magnon variety of man.

The Cro-Magnons were about 5 feet 11 inches in height, with a brain capacity in the larger representatives of 1660 c.c., a straight face, a well-developed, projecting nose, a high forehead, and a strong jaw. They made the most beautiful bone implements associated with an industry known as Aurignacian (from Aurignac in France where they were first found). Furthermore, the Cro-Magnons are believed to be the people who made some of the masterly paintings on the walls of caves, and the sculptures sometimes found in them, which have been discovered in many different parts of Europe. Perhaps the wall paintings in Lascaux Cave are the most famous of these.

Cro-Magnon man is a modern man in every sense of the word, but where he came from or how he came about we have not the slightest idea.

5

The Rise of Modern Man

AT ONE TIME, things used to be quite simple when anthropologists discussed the origin and evolution of man. Modern man was the last and highest type of man to be evolved. The most primitive type of man was held to be *Pithecanthropus erectus* or possibly *Pithecanthropus robustus*. All the types of men in between the pithecanthropines and modern man were held to be simply intermediate stages in the evolution of man from the most primitive to the most advanced type. However, certain finds of fossil man made in recent years render this earlier and apparently perfectly logical interpretation of the evolution of man seriously open to question.

Swanscombe Man

In 1935–36 there were found in the Barnfield gravel quarry at Swanscombe in Kent, England, two skull bones, the left parietal and the complete occipital bone, of a single individual in a Middle Pleistocene deposit associated with tools of typically Acheulian industry. In 1955 the right parietal bone was discovered. Except for being slightly thicker, these bones might in every way fit a modern head. Some authorities say that the face might not have been modern. This is a possibility, but a remote one. Were Swanscombe the only example of the kind, we might put it in the "suspense account." But there are others, and therefore we must pay Swanscombe the attention it deserves.

Fontéchevade Man

In a cave near the village of Montbrun in the Department of Charente, France, in a deposit of the Third Interglacial period, there the portions of two skulls were discovered, associated with artifacts of Tayacian industry. The Tayacian industry always precedes the Mousterian industry which is associated with Neanderthal man. So that we can be fairly certain that Fontéchevade man preceded Neanderthal man.

Fontéchevade I is represented by a beautifully preserved fragment of the region above the nose and the upper margin of the left orbit. This is a critically important part of the skull because it tells us at a glance what the forehead and facial region were like in the complete skull. In this type, almost all authorities are agreed, the face was exactly as in modern man. Fontéchevade I was either of late adolescent age or a young adult female.

Fontechévade II is represented by an almost complete skullcap. Facial bones and base of skull are missing. But again, except for thickness of bones, this is in every way a modern-like skull. The brain capacity was about 1470 c.c.

In Fontéchevade man we see yet another type with which

TABLE 3. CHRONOLOGICAL-CULTURAL TABLE OF THE DIVISIONS OF PREHISTORY AND OF THE HISTORIC PERIOD

Age	Alpine and Scandinavian glacial oscillations with corresponding changes of sea level and climate	Approximate dates	Principal Culture Stages of Europe, Egypt, and the Near East			Human Types
			Northwestern Continental Europe	West Central Europe	Egypt and the Near East	
Power Tools — STEEL		A.D. 1900	Rise of the Age of Power Tools			Persisting Varieties of Homo sapiens
New PIO		A.D. 1850	Steel Age Develops			
Old PIO	Present conditions of Mya Period in Baltic area	A.D. 1700	Steel (carbonized iron)			
IRON (Late)		A.D. 1000	Viking Age			
		A.D. 500	Roman Period of Iron Age			
(Middle)		50 B.C.	Iron Age Introduced	Historic Times		
		500 B.C.		Iron Age Introduced		
(Early)		1000 B.C.			Iron Age Begins	
BRONZE		1500 B.C.	Bronze Age Introduced			
	Final land rise in Baltic area or Late Tapes Period	2000 B.C.	Traces of Copper	Bronze Age Introduced	Bronze Age Begins	
COPPER		2500 B.C.	Late Neolithic with thick poll ax	Copper Age Introduced	Alloys in use	
NEO-LITHIC (Late)		3000 B.C.	Middle Neolithic with thin poll ax	Late Neolithic	History Begins / Writing Invented	
		3500 B.C.			Amratian industry	
		4000 B.C.			Use of Iron Begins	
NEO-LITHIC (Middle)	Sea rising, Ragunda retreat, with Littorina Sea (Early Tapes Period) preceded by late Ancylus Lake	4500 B.C.	Early Neolithic: Shell mound or Campignian industry Ertebølle industries	Middle Neolithic or Robenhausian industry	Agriculture and the Domestication of Animals	
		5000 B.C.	Norse industry with petroglyphs	Early Neolithic or Campignian and Asturian industries	Badarian industry	
		5500 B.C.	Maglemose industry		Use of Copper Begins	
		6000 B.C.				
MESO-LITHIC (Early)	Ragunda pause with Ancylus Lake	6500 B.C.	Lyngby industry	Azilian, Tardenoisian, and Capsian industries	Tasian industry	
		?800 B.C				

	Glacial stages	Date		Late Magdalenian		Chancelade
U P P E R · **P A L E O L I T H I C**	Fini-Glacial pause with Baltic ice-lake	8500 B.C.		Early Magdalenian and Capsian industries	Probable beginning of Neolithic culture in Nile valley floor silts	Předmost Cro-Magnon *Baker's Hole* Rhodesian
	Gothi-Glacial retreat with Baltic ice-lake	13,500 B.C.		Solutrean industry. Late Aurignacian industry	Sebilian industry of Nile valley terrace silts	Châtelperron Grimaldi, Cro-Magnon Africanthropus, Solo
	Gothi-Glacial pause with Baltic ice-lake			Early Aurignacian or Châtelperronian and Capsian industries		
M I D D L E	Würm or Achen and Dani-Glacial retreats with Frankfort and Pomeranian pause. Flandrian terrace	18,500 B.C.		Final Mousterian of the caves	Late Mousterian of the 10 ft. Nile terrace	Boskop
	Würm and Brandenburg or Dani-Glacial advances, 4TH GLACIAL	50,000 B.C.		Mousterian of the caves		Florisbad, Skhūl, Gibraltar II *Wadjak*
	Riss retreat with Monastirian terrace. 3RD INTER-GLACIAL. Hot summer	75,000 B.C.		Contemporary Acheulian, Early Mousterian, Tayacian, Micoquian. Levalloisian, and Clactonian industries from Somme terrace, etc.	Early Mousterian of the 30 ft. Nile terrace	*London*, Tabūn, Neanderthal, Ehringsdorf Fontéchevade, Solo Montmaurin
L O W E R	Riss and Polonian Advances. 3RD GLACIAL	150,000 B.C.		Derived implements		
		250,000 B.C.				*Steinheim* Swanscombe *Gigantopithecus* Heidelberg Sinanthropus, Atlanthropus Pithecanthropus erectus
	Mindel retreat with Tyrhenian terrace. 2ND INTER-GLACIAL	450,000 B.C.		Acheulian and contemporary Abbevillian and Clactonian industries from 2nd and Somme terrace. Clacton-on-Sea, Mesvin, etc.	Acheulian industry of the 50 ft. Nile terrace	
	Mindel advance. 2ND GLACIAL	550,000 B.C.		Derived implements		Pithecanthropus robustus
	Günz retreat with Milazzian terrace. 1ST INTERGLACIAL	600,000 B.C.		Proto-Abbevillian industry from below the Cromer forest beds and 3rd Somme terrace	Abbevillian and Early Abbevillian industries of the 100 ft. Nile terrace	Pithecanthropus (Modjokerto) *Meganthropus* *Kanam*
	Günz Advance. 1ST GLACIAL			Pre-Abbevillian or Ipswichian flake industry of East Anglian Crag formations	?	
ARCHEO-LITHIC	PLEISTOCENE			Pre-Abbevillian or Ipswichian flake industry of subcrag formations		
	PLIOCENE Donau with Sicilian terrace	1,000,000 yrs.	Eolithic stage?	Eolithic stage?	Eolithic stage?	

In using this table it should be understood that the approximate dates assigned to the different "Ages" refer only, in a general way, to the areas mentioned. As the table indicates these "Ages" were not everywhere contemporaneous. The different "Ages" do not afford a measure of time, for they varied in different parts of the world both in the time of their appearance and in their duration, while some of the cultural stages they embrace never appeared at all, but were completely skipped in the progress from one cultural stage to another. These ages are, therefore to be regarded as *cultural or technological* rather than as *chronological* periods. It is extremely important to grasp this fact. There was no world-wide evolution from one stage to another, nor did the several stages begin and end simultaneously all over the world. Thus, to give a simple example, the Early Iron Age began in Asia Minor about 1200 B.C., in central Europe about 900 B.C., in Italy about 1000 B.C., in China about 700 B.C., in southern England about 600 B.C., in Japan about A.D. 200, and in Fiji about 1872. In the last column names in *italics* refer to types which are uncertainly dated.

Gibbon   *Chimpanzee*   *Gorilla*

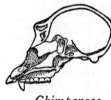 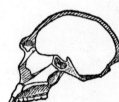

Chimpanzee   *Pithecanthropus*
Face restored
by Prof. J. H. McGregor

Chimpanzee   *Orangutan*   *Primitive*
Neanderthaloid
(Ehringsdorf)

FIG. 20   *Comparison of the brains, mid-sagittal sec*

Pithecanthropus
Based on a study
f the original skull top
Prof. J. H. McGregor

Neanderthal Man
(Chapelle-aux-Saints)

Modern Man

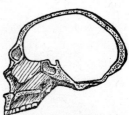

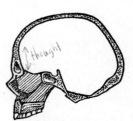

Neanderthal Man
(Chapelle-aux-Saints)
By Prof. J. H. McGregor

Cro-Magnon Man
By Prof. J. H. McGregor

Heidelberg Man

Neanderthal Man
(Chapelle-aux-Saints)

Cro-Magnon
Man

Modern
White Man

ons, and inner sides of lower jaws of anthropoids and man

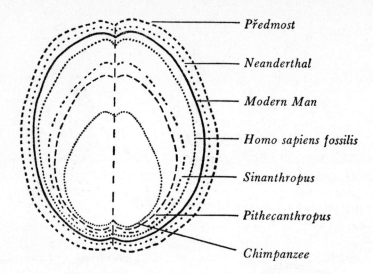

Předmost

Neanderthal

Modern Man

Homo sapiens fossilis

Sinanthropus

Pithecanthropus

Chimpanzee

FIG. 21 *A comparison of brain sizes, Chimpanzee, 400 c.c.* Pithecanthropus, *860 c.c.* Sinanthropus, *1075 c.c.* Homo sapiens fossilis, *1300 c.c. Modern man, 1400 c.c. Neanderthal man, 1450 c.c. Předmost, 1500 c.c.*

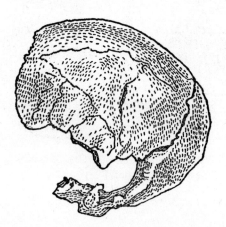

FIG. 22 *Left lateral view of the Swanscombe skull*

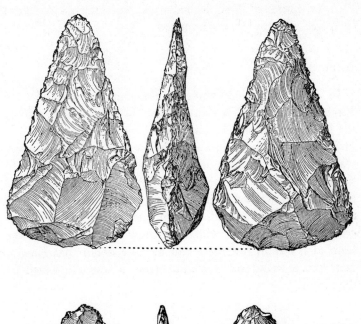

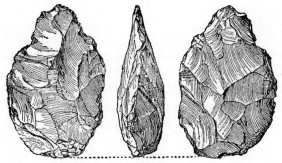

FIG. 23   *Acheulian hand axes associated with the Swanscombe
skull*

the forerunners of Neanderthal man, and later Neanderthal man himself, may have intermixed.

Kanam Man

In 1932 at West Kanam, on the southern shores of the Kavirondo Gulf of Victoria Nyanza, in Kenya, East Africa, the front portion of a human lower jaw was discovered. The importance of this mandible lies in the fact that it is in every way completely modern in appearance, yet it is claimed to have been recovered from a Lower Pleistocene deposit (now unfortunately washed away), which would make the Kanam mandible very old indeed. Kanam man suffered from a cancer of the chin region, which overgrew that structure in the form of a tumor, but there can be little doubt that Kanam man had a well-developed chin before it was obliterated by the tumor.

Kanjera Man

At Kanjera in Kenya, East Africa, the skeletal remains of three individuals of modern Negroid type were found in a Middle Pleistocene deposit associated with implements of Acheulian industry, that is to say of the same age and industry as Swanscombe man in England.

The Early Appearance of Neanthropic Man

Swanscombe, Fontéchevade, Kanam, and Kanjera man are representatives of the modernlike type of man, yet they appeared extremely early in the history of man's evolution. It therefore becomes a reasonable theory to assume that the modernlike type of man is much more ancient than was previously supposed, and it is quite possible that Neanderthal man, for example, is the product of admixture between such types as Solo with neanthropic man, rather than being a descendant of *Pithecanthropus* or Solo man in the direct line.

The older notion of straight-line evolution from ape to increasingly more advanced types of man is essentially sound, though in its oversimplified form of more advanced types appearing in a continuous straight line from less advanced types, it requires substantial modification.

Evolution is not best likened to a straight line but rather to a reticulum or network, in which all sorts of crisscrossing lines (groups) go in all sorts of directions, with interconnections established between the different cords of the network.

As a matter of fact, if we want to study the processes which have been operative in the past in giving rise to the varieties of men as we know them today, we can do no better than to observe them as they are occurring at the present time. This we shall do in the next chapter. In the present one let us briefly turn our attention to a particular aspect of the history of early man, the peopling of the Americas.

Early Man in the Americas

The evidence thus far uncovered suggests that man did not arrive in the Americas earlier than twenty-five thousand years ago. It is generally agreed that he probably entered the American land mass from Siberia across the Bering Strait, which even at the present time represents a distance across water of only fifty-six miles. During winter it is actually possible to walk across the strait, and it is easily navigable by boat.

The people who entered the Americas by this route were

mostly of Mongoloid origin, though it would seem that some non-Mongoloids or Caucasoid (white) populations may have entered too. This last statement is made on the basis of the fact that many Indians, even before admixture with whites, were known to exhibit predominantly Caucasoid characteristics.

KEY TO MAP ON FACING PAGE

MACKENZIE AREA: 1. *Kutchin;* 2. *Ingalik;* 3. *Tanana;* 4. *Tanaina;* 5. *Han;* 6. *Dog Rib;* 7. *Yellow Knife;* 8. *Tahltan;* 9. *Slave;* 10. *Sekani;* 11. *Beaver;* 12. *Chipewayan;* 13. *Tsimshian;* 14. *Sarsi;* 15. *Carrier*

NORTHWEST COAST: 1. *Tlingit;* 2. *Tsimshian;* 3. *Haida;* 4. *Kwakiutl;* 5. *Nootka;* 6. *Coast;* 7. *Salish;* 8. *Chinook;* 9. *Takelma;* 10. *Hupa;* 11. *Yurok*

PLATEAU: 1. *Thompson;* 2. *Okanagan;* 3. *Flathead;* 4. *Nez Perce;* 5. *Bannock;* 6. *Snake;* 7. *Klamath*

SOUTHWESTERN: 1. *Navaho;* 2. *Hopi;* 3. *Tewa;* 4. *Keresan;* 5. *Zuñi;* 6. *Havasupai;* 7. *Mohave;* 8. *Yuma;* 9. *Pima;* 10. *W. Apache;* 11. *Mescalero;* 12. *Seri;* 13. *Papago;* 14. *Tarahumara;* 15. *Yaqui;* 16. *Mayo*

CALIFORNIA BASIN: 1. *Klamath;* 2. *Modoc;* 3. *N. Shoshoni;* 4. *Paviotso;* 5. *Shoshoni;* 6. *Karok;* 7. *Miwok;* 8. *Pomo;* 9. *Mono;* 10. *Yokuts;* 11. *Salinan;* 12. *Southern Paiute;* 13. *Ute;* 14. *Mohave*

THE PLAINS: 1. *Blackfoot;* 2. *Assiniboine;* 3. *Gros Ventre;* 4. *Flathead;* 5. *Crow;* 6. *Bannock;* 7. *Mandan;* 8. *Hidatsa;* 9. *Arikara;* 10. *Dakota;* 11. *Ponca;* 12. *Omaha;* 13. *Osage;* 14. *N. Shoshoni;* 15. *Arapaho;* 16. *Cheyenne;* 17. *Kiowa;* 18. *Wichita;* 19. *Comanche;* 20. *Mescalero;* 21. *Caddo;* 22. *Tonkawa;* 23. *Lipan*

NORTHEASTERN: 1. *Naskapi;* 2. *Cree;* 3. *Montagnais;* 4. *Beothok;* 5. *Assiniboine;* 6. *Ojibwa;* 7. *Ottawa;* 8. *Dakota;* 9. *Fox;* 10. *Sauk;* 11. *Menomini;* 12. *Winnebago;* 13. *Kickapoo;* 14. *Iowa;* 15. *Illinois;* 16. *Miami;* 17. *Algonquin;* 18. *Huron;* 19. *Iroquois;* 20. *Erie;* 21. *Micmac;* 22. *Abenaki;* 23. *Penobscot;* 24. *Massachusetts;* 25. *Lenape;* 26. *Powhatan*

SOUTHEASTERN: 1. *Shawnee;* 2. *Cherokee;* 3. *Yuchi;* 4. *Chickasaw;* 5. *Creek;* 6. *Lipan;* 7. *Tonkawa;* 8. *Natchez;* 9. *Choctaw;* 10. *Seminole;* 11. *Timucua*

MEXICAN: 1. *Tepehuane;* 2. *Huichol;* 3. *Cora;* 4. *Otomi;* 5. *Aztec;* 6. *Tarascan;* 7. *Zapotecan;* 8. *Maya*

FIG. 24   *Areas of Indian culture and principal tribes*
in North America

FIG. 25   *Areas of Indian culture and principal tribes in South America*

There were probably several waves of migrations of different populations, some of whom made their way down to the very tip of South America, namely Tierra del Fuego. We know with certainty that men were already living in Tierra del Fuego at least nine thousand years ago, and they were probably there much earlier.

Some of the sites in which human remains have been found either in the form of human bones or human artifacts are listed in Table 4 with the estimated age of these remains, established wherever possible by the radiocarbon method.

The Radiocarbon Method of Dating

It was possible to say two paragraphs ago that we know with certainty that man was living in Tierra del Fuego at least nine thousand years ago because in recent years a reliable method of dating ancient remains has become available. This is known as the radiocarbon method.

The radiocarbon method of dating ancient remains depends upon the fact that radioactive carbon (Carbon 14), which is liberated in the atmosphere in consequence of the interaction of cosmic rays with nitrogen, is present in the structure of all

---

KEY TO MAP ON FACING PAGE

ANTILLEAN: 1. *Carib*

CHIBCHAN: 1. *Cuna;* 2. *Chibcha*

ANDEAN: 1. *Quitu;* 2. *Quechua;* 3. *Aymara;* 4. *Atacama;* 5. *Calchaqui*

AMAZONIAN: 1. *Bare;* 2. *Arawak;* 3. *Wapisiana;* 4. *Tama;* 5. *Macusis;* 6. *Moxos;* 7. *Witoto;* 8. *Boro;* 9. *Jivaro;* 10. *Manaos;* 11. *Apiaka;* 12. *Piro;* 13. *Chacabo;* 14. *Bororo;* 15. *Tupi;* 16. *Tupinamba;* 17. *Kaingua*

SOUTHWESTERN: 1. *Chono;* 2. *Alacalaf;* 3. *Yahgan*

ONAN: 1. *Ona*

PATAGONIAN: 1. *Pehuenche;* 2. *Puelche;* 3. *Tehuelche*

CHACO: 1. *Choroti;* 2. *Mataco;* 3. *Toba;* 4. *Pilaga;* 5. *Macori;* 6. *Abipone*

EAST BRAZILIAN: 1. *Canella;* 2. *Cayapo;* 3. *Kaingang;* 4. *Bakairi;* 5. *Charante;* 6. *Botocudo;* 7. *Cayapo*

living things. During their lives all living things maintain a
constant percentage of Carbon 14 in their carbon structure.
This percentage is the same for every form of life. At death
the assimilation of carbon and Carbon 14 ceases, and the

TABLE 4. SOME SITES AND LOCALITIES IN NORTH AMERICA
ASSOCIATED WITH HUMAN REMAINS

Site	Locality	Years Ago
Pinto Basin	Riverside County, California	2,000+
Lake Mohave	Lake Mohave, southeastern California	3,000+
Borax Lake	Borax Lake, California	3,000+
Leonard Rock	Pershing County, Nevada	7,038±350
Sulphur Springs	Sulphur Springs, Arizona	7,756±370
Signal Butte	Scotts Bluff County, western Nebraska	8,000+
Fort Rock Cave	Fort Rock, Oregon	9,053±350
Lime Creek	Lime Creek, Frontier County, Nebraska	9,524±450
Folsom	Near Folsom, New Mexico	9,883±350
Lindenmeier	South of Colorado-Wyoming boundary, northern Colorado	10,000+
Clovis-Portales	Between Clovis and Portales, central-eastern New Mexico	10,000+
Vero Beach	Vero, central-eastern Florida	10,000
Great Salt Lake	Great Salt Lake, Utah	10,000
Gypsum Cave	Frenchman Mountains, east of Las Vegas, Nevada	10,455±340
Sandia	Northern part of Sandia Mountains, New Mexico	15,000
Cochise	Whitewater Draw, northwest of Douglas, southeastern Arizona	15,000
Ventana Cave	Castle Mountains, southern Arizona	15,000

Carbon 14 atoms begin to disintegrate. Disintegration of Carbon 14 atoms proceeds at a constant rate, 15.3 atoms per minute per gram of carbon. The rate of disintegration of Carbon 14 was checked on samples of known age, yielding, in general, the most satisfactorily accurate results. The studies of Professor

W. F. Libby and his colleagues at the University of Chicago have shown that after $5,568 \pm 30$ years have elapsed, one half of the Carbon 14 isotopes have disintegrated. After about 11,136 years only a quarter of the atoms will be left, and so on. The radio-carbon method will give reliable results as far back as 50,000 years. One of its disadvantages is that to test bone it is necessary to have a few pounds of it, and this much can hardly be spared from the precious human bones unearthed, even in those cases when they are available in quantity. However, it is possible to test associated materials, and of these only a few ounces are required.

6

The Evolutionary Factors Involved in the Differentiation of Man

We have seen that in the prehistoric period there were many different types of men. Today in a land such as the United States we see types of men drawn from the most diverse populations all over the world. There are American Indians, the original inhabitants of America, there are whites of different origins, Mongoloids, Polynesians, Negroes, and Asiatic Indians. The members of all these groups are fundamentally alike and superficially different. How did all those differences which physically distinguish the different ethnic groups from one another come into being?

The answer, so far as we know it, is a very interesting story.

Unity Without Uniformity

Most authorities agree that all men have originated from a common ancestral stock. What that stock was, and when the diversification commenced, we do not know. But whatever the stock was we can be sure that the diversification did not proceed in straight lines, that whatever ethnic groups originated from that stock did not pursue their development independently of all the other ethnic groups. On the contrary, as we have already pointed out, such groups almost certainly met with others and interbred with them, a process which was undoubtedly often repeated. There is a unity, therefore, to mankind without any uniformity.

All men belong to the same genus *Homo* and the same species *sapiens*. Of this species there are many *varieties,* a word well chosen because it indicates that the different ethnic groups of men are merely the variations on a common theme which life plays to produce the great harmony of humanity— a state toward which mankind is increasingly tending in spite of any appearances to the contrary. Just as the black and white keys on the piano are necessary to the production of great music, so the colored and the white peoples of the earth are necessary to the harmony of the world.

It will help us to understand this better if we consider the nature of the factors which have produced the differentiations that we recognize in the varieties or ethnic groups of man.

The Factors Producing Human Differentiation

Beginning as a single human population early in the history of man, some families must have wandered off and set up separate domiciles at considerable distances from each other; and so in the course of time these isolated groups became populations in their own right, and upon them the following factors played their roles in producing evolutionary change: (1) natural selection, (2) mutation, (3) isolation, (4) genetic drift, (5) hybridization, (6) sexual selection, and (7) social selection.

Natural Selection

On the fifth page of his epoch-making book *The Origin of Species* (1859) Charles Darwin 1809–82 defined natural selection in the following words: "As many more individuals of each species are born than can possibly survive; and as, consequently, there is a frequently recurring struggle for existence, it follows that any being, if it vary however slightly in any manner profitable to itself, under the complex and sometimes varying conditions of life, will have a better chance of surviving, and thus be *naturally selected*. From the strong principle of inheritance, any selected variety will tend to propagate its new and modified form."

Today we speak of Darwinian fitness or adaptive fitness, meaning that such variations that arise and are beneficial to an organism tend, through the action of the environment, to be preserved, so that the possessors tend to leave a greater progeny behind them. For the latter reason a good short statement of natural selection is contained in the phrase "differential fertility." Those who possess adaptively valuable qualities in their particular environment will be at an advantage in comparison with those who do not possess such qualities, and the former are likely to flourish and the latter not to do so well.

Most characters, if not all, possessed by human beings are of adaptive value.

Dark-pigmented skin is of greater adaptive value than lightly pigmented skin in regions of high sunlight intensity and high humidity. The dark pigments absorb the light rays, which in the form of heat initiate sweating, thus causing water to carry off the heat of the body and at the same time to deposit a film of salts over the surface of the body. This film then serves to reduce and reflect the dangerous light rays from the surface of the body. In regions of low sunlight intensity as much light needs to be absorbed by the body as possible, hence a lightly pigmented skin is of adaptive value in such regions.

A broad nose is also useful in high temperature areas because this presumably permits the maximum exhalation of heated air. The narrow nose is of adaptive value in cooler climes where the air needs to be warmed before it is taken into the lungs.

Different environments call for different adaptive characters, and the different characters which human beings exhibit are principally due to the fact that man has had to adapt himself to whatever environment in which he has found himself. Being perhaps the most adaptable of all creatures, it is not surprising that he should exhibit such a remarkably interesting variety of adaptive traits.

Mutation

A mutation is a transmissible change in the structure of a hereditary particle or gene, the giant protein molecule whose biochemical components constitute the biological bases of heredity. Mutations are the raw materials of the evolutionary process. Without mutation there can be no significant evolutionary change. Mutations are constantly occurring in all populations. It is believed that at least one mutation occurs in every human being sometime between conception and death.

The kinky hair of Negroes is almost certainly due to a mutation having adaptive value, but what that adaptive value may be we do not know. All the anthropoid apes have straight hair. The inference is that the original ancestral group of man had straight hair, but that subsequent mutations in the ancestry of the Negroid group gave rise to kinky hair. Sometimes kinky hair appears in a white family as a mutation. There are several such families recorded in Scandinavia in which there can be no question of any but white ancestry.

Mutations having adaptive value would rapidly become established in the small populations which were characteristic of early man.

Isolation

The earth is a very large place, and upon its surface men have lived in small groups, isolated from one another for long periods of time, until the very recent period. Isolation means here the separation of a group from all other groups of the same species, so that breeding takes place completely or largely within the isolated group alone. Isolation is brought about by such natural factors as distance, mountain ranges, rivers, forests, seas, and the like.

Under conditions of isolation and random mutation—all mutation being random—every isolated group, no matter how like other groups it originally was, would more or less rapidly become distinguishable from all other groups by virtue of the differences in the mutations which would arise in each group. This fact makes isolation an inseparable factor from the phenomenon of genetic drift.

Genetic Drift

This phenomenon, first described by Professor Sewall Wright of the University of Chicago, is sometimes spoken of as "the Sewall Wright effect." It has already been pointed out that the populations of man up to the Neolithic or New

Stone Age were very small. For example, two great authorities, Professors Herbert J. Fleure and Graham Clark, have independently estimated that the total population of Britain (now 50 million) in Upper Paleolithic times (under a sub-glacial climate) was between 250 and 2,000, probably nearer 250 in winter months. At the present day peoples in the lower hunter stage of cultural development, such as the Australian aborigines and the Eskimos, seldom reach a population size of over 400.

In such small populations, owing to the sampling nature of the hereditary mechanism, it is possible for mutations having no particular adaptive value to survive and spread throughout the particular population. All one needs is time and isolation, and the random variation presented by mutation will turn up a number of neutral mutations which may become established in the population. What these are likely to be no one could possibly predict because they are random in their appearance. Such mutations due to chance fluctuations may increase or become extinguished.

Hybridization

This has, in the past, been a much-neglected factor in considering the differentiation of man. Hybridization simply means the mating of individuals differing from one another in one or more genes or characters. There are two kinds of hybridization: (1) between individuals, and (2) between populations. Both types of hybridization have played important roles in the evolution of mankind.

During hybridization, and as a net effect of hybridization, both the groups involved bring to each other their valuable biological traits and thus serve to compensate for any deficiencies which the other group may be carrying. Hence deficiencies which are brought to the mating process are generally canceled out. Hybridization has, therefore, a powerful creative effect. Not only does it produce the modification of physical characters, but it produces also the modification of physiological ones, and thus serves to increase the adaptive value of the offspring. As a result of such matings, there is generally an increase in size, fecundity, resistance to disease, and other adaptive qualities—just as is the case in hybrid corn or hybrid animals. This phenomenon is known as *hybrid vigor*.

Sexual Selection

It is not certain what part sexual selection has played in the past in the evolution of man. Sexual selection means the selection by the most powerfully endowed males of the most preferred females. "Powerfully endowed" may mean many different things. In one group it may mean the possession of the greatest muscular power, in another the greatest social prestige as a result of the ownership of property, in yet another it may mean being the kindest person, and in still another being the most loved, and so on. Such men may be in a favored position to choose what women they will marry or mate with. It is probable that to some extent sexual selection in this sense has been operative in the past in the evolution of man.

Actually it would seem that sexual selection has been rather more of a factor in the recent past—probably becoming an increasingly more important one in the future—than it has been in the remote past. For not only are women being selected by males for their attractive qualities, but women are beginning to exercise their free choice for the first time on a large scale.

The preference of males for fat women in some societies tends to favor the increase of such body types in these societies. In America, mating between whites and Negroes and the preference of darker Negroes for lighter Negro females tends to lighten, in the long run, Negro skin color. Among whites, the preference of brunets of one sex for blondes of the other, and vice versa, is an example of the manner in which a balanced distribution of such types may be maintained in a society.

Social Selection

In all populations social distinctions are instituted between individuals or groups of individuals. There are chieftains, members of the council, medicine men, sorcerers, accomplished hunters, great braves, members of the royal family, the nobility, the upper classes, the middle classes, the lower classes, and so on.

In nonliterate societies marriage does not proceed at random but is usually strictly regulated. Such regulations often determine the breeding structure of the population in such a way that distinct differences may be produced between different segments of the population. In our own time we have certain outstanding examples of this: the Hapsburg jaw characteristic of many members of the Spanish royal family; bleeders' disease, or hemophilia, exhibited by a proportion of the male descendants of Queen Victoria, in which royal lady the mutation for this disorder most probably occurred; the insanity that afflicted many members of the house of Hanover. Intermarriage with women of good stock has resulted in the virtual elimination of the latter unfortunate affliction in the descendants of this house, who have occupied the throne of England for the last hundred years.

In earlier times social selection probably played its part in the differentiation of populations and of groups within those populations. If by social selection we understand the regulation of breeding between socially distinguished individuals or groups within a population, so that mating occurs between

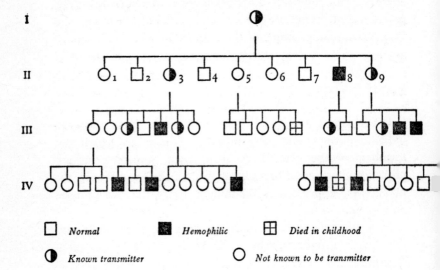

FIG. 26 *Hemophilic pedigree originating with Queen Victoria*
circles = female; squares = male

individuals preferred by such social standards, rather than at random, we may predict that social selection will continue to play a part in the differentiation of man, both within populations and between populations.

The Process of Differentiation

The material given above is actually an account of the manner in which the so-called "races" of man have come into being. The term "race" has been confused by so much emotion and false meaning that it is better not to use it at all in the case of man. The noncommittal term or phrase "ethnic group" is much better. An ethnic group is any population which as a group is distinguishable from another population on the basis of physical characters.

In the course of the physical differentiation of man, man has also had to adapt himself culturally to his many different environments, that is to say, he has had to work out a way of life best fitted to the particular environment in which he found himself. The particular way in which a people adapts itself to its environment behaviorally is called its *culture*. There has been a cultural differentiation of man as well as a physical one. Because cultures vary, and often vary with a difference of ethnic group, some people have erroneously concluded that culture and "race" are associated. This is to commit the fallacy of thinking that because two things are associated, one is the cause of the other. This is, of course, absurd.

The Mental Unity of Man and the Variety of Human Cultures

The outstanding characteristic of man is that he is the most educable, the most intellectually malleable, the most plastic of all creatures. Everything he knows as a human being, man has had to learn from other human beings. The evidence, as scientists have been able to reveal it, indicates that the average person in any human society is able to learn just as much as the average person in any other society.

Insofar as behavior is concerned, evolution has not proceeded to differentiate human populations into specialists able to meet the requirements of a particular environment and no others, but, on the contrary, the evolution of man has proceeded in such a way that he has become a creature capable of adapting to *all* environments.

Indeed, as we study human beings in all societies we find that the one trait which is at a premium in human society is *adaptability,* plasticity, the ability to get along with others, to adjust to rapidly changing conditions. It is not any special ability which is emphasized, but rather this general ability of adaptability, plasticity. And we may be sure that it has been so throughout the history of man's sojourn on this planet. If this is so, then it constitutes a strong argument for the mental unity of mankind on an evolutionary basis, and an argument for the cultural differentiation of humanity on precisely the same basis. Human beings anywhere can learn to do the things that other human beings have anywhere done.

Now that the airplane has put the most distant place on the earth no more than forty-five hours away, the tendency of human populations is the opposite of what it was in the prehistoric period, when small populations tended to migrate away from a common center toward the periphery of the earth. Today human populations are tending to come together physically. It is our immediate task, and it will be the realization of the future, to enable the peoples of the earth to come together culturally and spiritually. Then all mankind will once again become truly one—maintaining, it is to be hoped, the differences as far as it is desirable to maintain them, and producing a genuinely creative, interanimating unity without a dulling uniformity.

7

The Ethnic Groups of Man

IF WE WANT to think and talk clearly about the different groups of mankind—and we shall increasingly have to do so as time goes on—it is desirable to have some scheme by which we can distinguish one group from another. Most classifications of the ethnic groups of mankind are based on the recognition of a similarity within each group of physical characters based on heredity.

There are three major groups of mankind: (1) the Negroid, (2) the Mongoloid, and (3) the Caucasoid. A major group is a complex of populations which are classified together because of a basic similarity of certain physical characters.

The Negroid Major Group

Characterized by dark brown skin, often almost ebony-black, and in some populations yellowish brown. The body hair is very sparse; the head hair varies from tightly curled to peppercorn (sparsely distributed tufts). The nose tends to be broad and rather flattish, the lips usually thick and everted, and there is some forward projection of the jaw. The ears tend to be small, the head long.

There are three subgroups: (1) African Negroids, (2) Oceanic Negroids, of the territory of New Guinea and the great group of islands extending to the east all the way to the Fiji Islands, and (3) Negroids of southeastern Asia, including the Andamanese of the Bay of Bengal, the Semangs of the Malay Peninsula and East Sumatra, and the Aetas of the Philippines.

The Mongoloid Major Group

The skin sometimes has a faintly yellowish tinge, and a fold of skin overhanging the inner angle of the eye opening—the epicanthic fold or Mongoloid fold—is present in most individuals. Body hair is very sparse, and head hair is black, lank, and fewer to the square centimeter than in Caucasoids.

Mongoloids inhabit northern, central, and southeastern Asia—embracing the Philippines, Malaysia, the East Indies—and the Americas, for the American Indians are members of this major group.

The Caucasoid Major Group

This group is commonly called white because of the "white" skin which characterizes most of its members. The name "Caucasoid" was given to the group by the father of physical anthropology, Johann Friedrich Blumenbach (1752–1840), who described the type from the skull of a female emanating from Georgia in the Caucasus.

The skin color varies from white to dark brown. The body

hair is usually well developed, and head hair varies from silky straight, wavy, to various degrees of curliness. It is never woolly, rarely frizzly, and is almost never as coarse or as sparsely distributed as in Mongoloids. The nose is comparatively narrow and projecting, the lips tend to be thin, and every form of head shape is encountered. The original habitat of the Caucasoids was Greater Europe; now they are widely spread over the face of the earth.

The Ethnic Groups of Man

An ethnic group is a distinct population within a major group. An ethnic group represents one of a number of populations, which together constitute a major group, but which individually maintain their differences, physical and cultural, by means of isolating mechanisms, such as geographic or social barriers. These differences will vary as the power of the geographic and social barriers vary. Where these barriers are of low power, neighboring ethnic groups will intergrade or hybridize with one another. Where these barriers are of high power, such ethnic groups will tend to remain distinct from each other or replace each other.

The following is a classification of the major and ethnic groups of man.

The Major and Ethnic Groups of Man

Major Group: NEGROID

African Negroes

Ethnic Groups: a. True Negro: West Africa, Cameroons, and the Congo

b. Hamite: East and northeastern Africa

    c. Nilo-Hamite: East Africa and east-central Africa
    d. Nilote or Nilotic Negro: eastern Sudan and Upper Nile Valley
    e. Forest Negro: equatorial and tropical Africa
    f. Bushman-Hottentot
    g. African Pygmy or Negrillo: equatorial Africa

Oceanic Negroids

Ethnic Groups: a. Papuan: New Guinea
      b. Melanesian: Melanesia
      c. New Guinea Pygmy or Negrito: New Guinea

Asiatic Pygmies or Negritos

Ethnic Groups: a. Andamanese: Andaman Islands
      b. Semang: central region of Malay Peninsula, and East Sumatra
      c. Aeta: Philippine Islands

Oceanic Pygmies or Negritos

Ethnic Group: a. New Guinea Pygmy: New Guinea

Major Group: MONGOLOID

Classical Mongoloids

Ethnic Groups: An undetermined number of ethnic groups in the older populations of Tibet, Mongolia, China, Korea, Japan, and Siberia, including such tribes as the Buriat east and west of

Lake Baikal, the Koryak of northern
Siberia, the Gilyak of northernmost
Sakhalin and the mainland north of
the Amur estuary (who appear to
have mixed with the Ainu), and the
Goldi on the Lower Amur and
Ussuri

Arctic Mongoloids

Ethnic Groups:
a. Eskimo: extreme northeast of Asia,
arctic coast of North America,
Greenland. The type includes the
Aleut of the Aleutian Islands, and
the Reindeer and coastal Chukchee
of northeastern Siberia
b. Evenki or True Tungus (American-
oid): Mongolia, Siberia, Asiatic
highlands north of the Himalayas
c. Kamtchadal: Kamchatka
d. Samoyede: Kola Peninsula, White
Sea and Yenisei regions

American Indians

Ethnic Groups:
a. An undetermined number of ethnic
groups of North, Central, and South
America

Indo-Malay Mongoloids

Ethnic Groups:
a. Indonesian: southern China, Indo-
China, Burma, Thailand, interior of
Malay Archipelago

        b. Malay: in addition to Indonesian distribution given above, Malay Peninsula, Dutch East Indies, Philippines, Okinawa, and adjacent islands

Major Group: CAUCASOID

Ethnic Groups: a. Basic Mediterranean: borderlands of the Mediterranean Basin
        b. Nordic: central Europe, Scandinavia, and neighboring regions
        c. East Baltic: eastern Baltic regions
        d. Lapp: northern Scandinavia, Kola Peninsula
        e. Alpine: France along the Alps to Russia
        f. Dinaric: eastern Alps from Switzerland to Albania, Asia Minor, and Syria
        g. Armenoid: Asia Minor
        h. Indo-Dravidian: India and Ceylon
        i. Polynesian: Polynesia

Major Subgroup: ARCHAIC CAUCASOID OR AUSTRALOID

Ethnic Groups: a. Australian: Australia
        b. Veddah: Ceylon
        c. Pre-Dravidian: India
        d. Ainu: Hokkaido (Yezo) and Sakhalin Islands, Japan

A Word in Conclusion

There have been many classifications of the "races" of mankind. The above is but one of them. With slight modifications, no doubt, it is one that would be accepted by most authorities. Nevertheless, it should be remembered that all classifications are arbitrary, and this one is as much subject to modification as others have been. The above classification is calculated to be helpful in thinking about the varieties of mankind; it is *not* intended to solidify anyone's views.

8

Needs and Culture

E VERY HUMAN BEING is born with certain basic needs, inborn needs which must be satisfied if the organism is to
survive. The basic needs are: oxygen, food, liquid, rest, activity, sleep, bowel and bladder elimination, escape from fright-
ening situations, and the avoidance of pain.

In connection with each of these basic needs, every human
being is subjected to the teaching of his culture. We all
breathe, eat, drink, rest, sleep, and eliminate in ways that we
have learned are the custom in our group, no matter what the
custom may be in other groups. We are all, to a certain extent
custom-made, tailored according to the prevailing pattern of
our society.

The Meaning of Culture

Because of man's great capacity for adaptability and his
remarkable ingenuity, he can improve in a great variety of

ways upon the manner in which the lower animals meet their needs. Within every society there are particular ways in which needs are met. The origin of these ways are usually "lost in the mists of antiquity" or, as the Australian aborigines say, they "belong in the dream time." In fact, one of the hardest things in anthropology is to trace the origin of a custom. There is usually no one old enough to remember its origin because as a rule it came into being a very long time ago, long before written history.

Culture represents man's response to his basic needs. Culture is man's way of making himself comfortable in the world. It is the behavior he has learned as a member of society. We may define culture as the way of life of a people, the environment which a group of human beings occupying a common territory have created in the form of ideas, institutions, pots and pans, language, tools, utensils, and sentiments.

The criteria by which culture may be recognized are: (1) It must be invented, (2) it must be transmitted from generation to generation, and (3) it must be perpetuated in its original or in modified form. While some lower animals are capable of very limited cultural behavior, man alone seems to be virtually unlimited in his capacity for culture. The process of creating, transmitting, and maintaining the past in the present is culture—the capacity which the American semanticist Alfred Korzybski called time-binding. Plants bind chemicals, animals bind space, but man alone binds time.

The Conditions of Human Culture

Man is human by virtue of the fact that he possesses certain potentialities which are developed to a uniquely high degree. He is born utterly dependent for his survival upon other human beings during his first few years, and in this dependency relationship, more prolonged than that of any other creature, he learns to develop those potentialities under the stimulating influence of a human environment. *Whatever we know and do as human beings, we have had to learn from other human beings.* Other creatures, on the other hand, have to learn very little by comparison. For most of what they do, they are equipped by instinct, that is by automatic response without reasoning or design. Man differs from all other creatures in the possession of the following characteristics, which at the same time constitute the conditions for the development of human culture:

1. Freedom from the instinctive, automatic responses to the environment that characterize animal behavior.
2. Extraordinarily plastic potentialities for the development of a complex intelligence. Educability.
3. A highly developed capacity for symbolic thought.
4. Speech.

The creature endowed with these qualities is in a position to interact in a creative manner with its environment—and that, precisely, is what human beings have done from the beginning of time.

The Development of Culture

When a man and a woman unite and produce a child, the biological family comes into being. The helplessness of the child renders necessary the expenditure of much time and energy on its care. Men and women who have united in such a social relationship will have to provide the infant with special comforts and protection. Domestic activities will have to be put on a new basis. The infant will have to be fed, cleaned, his needs attended to, and he will have to be trained.

Each parent will have to assume his or her special obligations and share somewhat different kinds of authority. The arrival of the child entails the development of a new relationship with the members of neighboring families and the social (legal) recognition of the new bonds which have been established between the parents and the child. In turn, recognition of the new bonds which have been created by the parents with the group must be established, for the parents have now become responsible to the group for the proper education of the child.

Such obligatory relationships will inevitably arise under the conditions described in all societies, and the economic, legal, educational, and political responses—that is, the responses growing out of the satisfaction of the basic needs, and of the new needs derived from the ways in which they are satisfied —in turn give rise to all or almost all of those cultural responses which we know. Most of these cultural responses may be fruitfully summarized in the following synopsis:

CULTURAL RESPONSES TO THE NEEDS OF
HUMAN BEINGS LIVING IN SOCIETY

1. Patterns of communication: gestures, language, writing, etc.
2. Material traits
   a. Food habits and food-getting
   b. Personal care and dress
   c. Shelter
   d. Utensils, tools, etc.
   e. Weapons
   f. Occupations and industries
   g. Transportation and travel
3. Exchange of goods and services: barter, trade, commerce

4. Forms of property: real and personal
5. Sex and family patterns
   a. Marriage and divorce
   b. Methods of reckoning relationships
   c. Guardianship
   d. Inheritance
6. Societal controls
   a. Mores
   b. Public opinion
7. Government
   a. Political forms
   b. Judicial and legal procedures
8. Religious and magical practices
9. Mythology and philosophy
10. Science
11. Art: carving, painting, drawing, dancing, music, literature, etc.
12. Recreational interests: sports, games, etc.

Culture and the Individual

No single individual ever gains a knowledge of the whole of his culture. As a member of his culture, the individual is equipped to participate in it, not to become a mere repository of it. Every individual is born with a unique biological endowment of potentialities which are like those of his fellows, but not exactly the same. This is the biological heredity of the individual. The culture into which the person is born constitutes his social heredity. The interaction between the individual's biological and social heredities is, in fact, what constitutes the person's *heredity*. There is no heredity without the interaction between one's biological equipment of potentialities and the environment or environments in which they undergo development. Human nature is not what a man is born with, but what he becomes under the organizing influence of the socializing environment into which he is born.

It is principally through the agency of the stimulation of the cultural environment that the individual becomes a person.

The Cooperative Nature of Man

A human baby is born not only wanting and needing to be loved, but also wanting and needing to love others. For too long we have erroneously believed that little babies are born rather selfish, aggressive little creatures, who need to be disciplined and repressed. This belief has done a great deal of damage to human beings and to society. We now know that all human beings are born with their needs oriented in the direction of love. The word "love" is used here to mean behavior which confers upon others survival benefits in such a manner that their potentialities for being human are afforded the opportunity for optimum development.

Every society exhibits this desire of human beings to live together in peace and creative harmony. Many societies at the same time exhibit the evidences of competition, sometimes even to the most violent degree. Such evidences constitute the symptoms of disorganization rather than of health. The general trend of human evolution in most human societies has been toward the achievement of cooperation between men rather than of conflict. By "cooperation" is meant striving together to achieve common goals. By "competition" is meant striving against others to achieve a goal. Cooperative competition, when it is in the interest of the group, can be healthy, but competitive competition for selfish interests is not.

An example of cooperative competition is any sport that

is played in such a manner as to bring out the best in the other players so that they in turn will be caused to bring out the best in us. In competitive competition one takes every possible advantage of the opposite side in order to win at any cost, rather than rejoicing in the fact that one has done one's skillful best and that the best team has won, whether it be one's own or the opposite side's.

Let us now consider how man adapts himself to the world in which he arrives naked and with a cry.

9

Attempting to Make the Best of It

HUMAN BEINGS are social creatures; they take pleasure in association, they become depressed in the absence of their fellows. Hence, one always considers man as a social being, and as such we find that the first experience to which he is usually exposed is the sound of the human voice. Even before he is offered nourishment, the human baby is greeted by his mother's voice or the voices of those who are assisting in its birth. The sound of the human voice is an experience for the human infant more constant than the experience of food.

Small infants learn to understand human sounds much earlier than was at one time thought possible, even though they do not begin to speak much before they are fourteen months old. What and how a human being speaks is learned largely from the members of his immediate cultural group. At the present time there are nearly three thousand languages in the world. Of these nearly three thousand languages, the vast majority fall into about thirty-five unrelated linguistic stocks or families.

Sometimes anthropologists are asked whether it is true that primitive languages don't have a grammar. The answer is that if there were any system of sounds that was grammarless, whatever else it might be, it certainly wouldn't be a language. Grammar comprises the formal rules by which the meanings of sounds are governed. The fact is that many "primitive" languages aren't any more primitive than most of the rest of the culture; indeed, they are often a great deal more complex and more efficient than the languages of the so-called higher civilizations.

As with all other things, man has been most inventive in his patterns of communication.

Language

Language is the communication of ideas by articulate sounds or words. We know practically nothing of the history of any language for the simple reason that the earliest written language, Sumerian cuneiform, goes back to about 3500 B.C. In comparison to the total history of man this represents less than five minutes of the human day.

Language comes into being when two or more individuals agree to attach the same meaning to the same sounds, and thereafter to use those sounds consistently with the meanings that have been conferred upon them. The meanings are symbols which stand for something which is actually not present to one's senses in physical form.

Every language has a definite phonetic system, that is, the sounds which are used are limited to a definite number of vowels and consonants. However, the actual sounds employed or neglected may differ very widely in different languages.

Similarly, languages differ even more markedly in their grammars. There are grammatical processes in American Indian languages, for example, which are quite unknown to languages of the great Indo-Germanic stock. Such a process, for example, is that of infixing, which means taking a particle of a word and putting it in the middle of another word or between the particles of several other words, and giving the sentence a modified meaning by doing so. In English we have affixes and suffixes but no real infixes, although the cockney's "abso-bloody-lutely" or "im-bloody-possible," which introduces a whole word into the middle of the original to give it greater intensity, is based on the principle. In sounds we have no clicks, but some languages like African Bantu are characterized by a well-developed system of meaningful clicks.

The Eskimos live among ice all their lives but have no single word for ice. This is not due to their stupidity, for they are very intelligent indeed, but rather to the fact that they have no need for such a word. What they do need are many words meaning the different states and conditions of ice: ice solid, ice melting, ice moving, ice breaking up, ice piling up, and so on. Their language reflects the practical uses to which it must be put. There are many nonliterate peoples who live in forested regions who have no word synonymous with our "tree." In this case, too, the language reflects practical need, and there are names for every kind of tree and every state of tree. Language reflects cultural interest, and for most peoples the meaning of a word is related to the action with which it is connected. As languages grow somewhat removed from practical need, they tend to become more abstract and unrelated to action. Language is marked by its great plasticity and its adaptability to the needs of the culture.

Where life is dependent upon sharply defined meanings, the language will reflect this. To most American Indians the statement "A dog is barking" sounds stupid. What *he* wants to know is *what* dog? *Whose* dog? *Where?* Is it standing, running, jumping, or what? In his own language he can say these things in as few sounds as we make when stating that a dog is barking. It is important for the Indian to have the kind of information he needs, and he would never think of being as vague as we are in speaking of a barking dog. Unlike ourselves, many nonliterate people have the capacity of saying a maximum number of things in a minimum number of words.

The analysis of language is complex and interesting but a vast subject, into which it would be impossible to enter any further here. We must conclude, then, with the statement that without language human culture would be impossible, and that granting man's great educability, he becomes even more educable through the exploitation of the new meanings that language, properly used, makes possible. Language is the great social stimulator and binder.

Some day, it is to be hoped, humanity will speak a single international language (without necessarily losing the advantages of the language of one's culture), and thus will the greatest obstacle to the communication between peoples be at once removed.

Gesture

Gesture has been described as an auxiliary language. Some peoples, such as the southeastern European Jews and the Italians, do, indeed, to some extent make use of gestures in this way, but there are many other peoples who either make no use of gestures at all—like the American Indian, who is traditionally known to be both laconic and undemonstrative, and like the English, who to some extent may be similarly characterized—or who make very little use of gesture such as the Melanesians of the Pacific.

Some Plains Indian peoples did elaborate a small inventory of gestures by which they were able to communicate with others, but these gestures were never a substitute for their spoken language, merely a supplement on occasion. There is no evidence that human language was ever preceded by a stage in which gestures alone were used for the purposes of communication.

Writing

Writing is written language. It is the method of communicating thoughts and feelings by means of visible signs. The earliest writing that we know is cuneiform (Latin: *cuneus, forma,* wedge-form) from Sumer in Mesopotamia in the valley of the Tigris and Euphrates rivers—the very birthplace of civilization itself. The date is about 3500 B.C. So writing is just about five thousand years old. The so-called primitive peoples of the world have no written language, and are

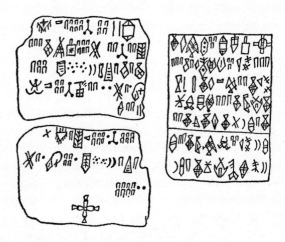

FIG. 27 *Earliest writing: Proto-Elamite*

therefore more appropriately spoken of as nonliterate. All peoples were nonliterate up to five thousand years ago. Egyptian hieroglyphics (sacred writing) are known from 3000 B.C. and are believed to have originated under the stimulus of Sumerian writing.

The forerunners of writing are known from cave drawings, from rock drawings, message sticks, tree inscriptions, and bark letters. Below is reproduced a letter from an American Indian girl to her lover. It is a letter, but it is not writing because it is not a formalized system of symbols which everyone would understand; the marks are private, not public, symbols.

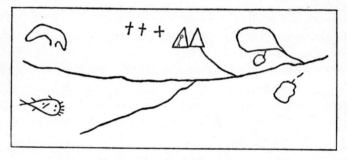

FIG. 28   *American Indian girl's letter*

The girl, who belongs to the bear totem, writes to her boy-friend, who belongs to the mud-puppy totem, that she would be glad to receive a visit from him, as indicated by the symbol of a hand drawn on the tipi which she occupies. The trail leads toward the lakes, shown by three irregular outlines, whence it branches off in the direction of the two tents, which are situated near those occupied by three Christian girls, indicated by the crosses.

Many American Indian tribes had a form of pictographic writing, and the Maya Indians seem to have had one, too. But these forms of pictographic writing were very limited in function. It was not until the development of urban civilization in Mesopotamia and Egypt that the necessity of keeping accounts gave rise to the invention of writing.

Other Forms of Communication

Forms of communication by "jungle telegraph" such as by drumbeat, smoke signals, whistling, hornblowing, cries, light, semaphore, and the like have been independently devised by many different peoples.

Food Habits and Food-Getting

The anthropoid apes are herbivores, that is to say, they live on a plant diet, and they have the long gut of all herbivores. So has man. Man has inherited a herbivorous gastrointestinal tract, but he is everywhere an omnivore, eating everything that is edible—even the most poisonous plants and animals after having eliminated the poison. Anthropoid apes spend most of their time eating. Man is similarly inclined, but as a result of his training he has in some cultures learned to regulate his habits of eating. The Italians call the English "the people of five meals"; to them it seems remarkable that anyone should want to eat so often, since they themselves eat only a very slight breakfast and only two other meals during the day.

Up to about eight thousand years ago all tribes of human beings lived by hunting, and most of them also by fishing, assisted by the picking of berries, fruits and nuts, and the digging for roots and tubers. Perhaps the first division of labor between the sexes was that the male became the hunter and the female the food-gatherer.

There are many peoples at the present day who still earn their living in this way, for example, the Australian aborigines, the Eskimos, the pygmies of central equatorial Africa, the Andaman Islanders, and the Onas of Tierra del Fuego, to mention but a few. Earning a livelihood by hunting and food-gathering means that populations must remain small and that they must continually wander over vast areas of land in order to avoid exhausting both the plant and animal life of a limited region. Such small populations, being nomadic, build no permanent habitations, and are equipped only with the lightest and minimum number of tools. Their imperma-nent shelters are, therefore, likely to be simple, like the Aus-tralian windbreak, which is built of the lightest twigs and grass and constitutes a protection against wind and sun. There are no pots or pans. Cooking is done over a fire with the food held on a skewer or the whole animal dumped on the fire.

Should one desire to boil water, all one does is dig a hole of the desired depth in the ground, harden the sides, pour the water in, and then drop stones which have been heated in a fire into the water. This method of heating water, many hun-dreds of thousands of years after it was first invented, may have caused some bright genius to think of taking the hole out of the ground, as it were, and making it portable in the form of a stone vessel or pot.

Not all hunters were nomads. If one feeds mainly on fish, for example, one may easily lead a settled life. The salmon-catching Indians of British Columbia built permanent plank houses in permanent villages. Handicrafts were perfected and wealth created, and with it nobles, commoners, and slaves.

Hunting and fishing calls for great resourcefulness. The Australian aborigines, for example, invented the boomerang, a unique hunting implement which will return to the thrower if it does not hit the target. They use spears, and spear-throwers which increase the power behind the spear. Since the Australian aboriginal of the interior lives in a desert or semidesert region, almost anything is eatable to him. Such an aboriginal will think nothing of catching a poisonous snake with his foot, picking it up, biting off its head, and then skinning and consuming it. Had we been brought up under similar conditions we would, no doubt, be happy to do the same.

The bow and arrow never reached Australia, but what early Edison invented it or where or when it was invented we do not know; it was probably invented somewhere in the Old World. It is found throughout Southeast Asia and the islands of the Pacific, in Africa, and in the Americas. The earliest evidence for the bow is from the Neolithic of Spain some ten thousand years ago, though it may very well have been invented in the Upper Paleolithic (Upper Old Stone Age).

Bolas are among the earliest hunting weapons that we know. These have been found in Middle Paleolithic sites, and their use still survives in South America and among the Eskimos. Bolas are made from a collection of weights, usually three, each weight being attached to a cord and each cord knotted at the end. The hunter holds the bola by the knotted cords at the end, and whirls the bola around his head and lets drive. The weights spread out and when they hit the target, usually a large bird, they wrap themselves around its legs and bring the animal down.

Nets, snares, and traps are widely used among hunting peoples, as are decoys. From cave paintings and rock drawings, it is clear that our prehistoric ancestors often disguised themselves as the animals they hunted and then freely moved among the herd. American Indians did this when hunting buffalo and bison, Eskimos do this sometimes when hunting reindeer, and the Bushmen of South Africa do this when hunting ostrich.

The ingenuity of hunting peoples in obtaining their food bears striking testimony to the great intelligence of the human species. It would take a very large book indeed to give an account of all the methods, but perhaps we can best conclude this section with an account of one of the cleverest traps, and one of the simplest, that man has ever developed.

This trap is designed to catch guinea fowl. It is known from Madagascar and many parts of Africa. It consists of a ring of clay about six to eight inches across and about one inch high, modeled on a flat rock. Some ground nuts are put in the circle. The nuts are a little too big for the fowl to pick up, but they keep on trying. Every time a fowl pecks at one and misses, its beak comes down hard on the rock. Being persistent creatures,

FIG. 29   *The Hunter of Les Trois Frères*

they keep this up until their heads swell and they go blind. The trap owner every day visits the brush near the trap and picks up the disabled birds. When chickens are raised on a concrete floor the same thing is likely to happen—as every poultry raiser knows.

Hunting peoples have no domestic animals with the exception of the dog, and many of them don't even have a dog. Some hunting peoples have learned to put the dog to use in hunting: the Onas of Tierra del Fuego, for example, use their dogs to scent out the guanaco (a deer-sized camel) and bring it to bay. The Australian aborigines love their dogs as pets; the dogs serve also as scavengers to keep the encampment clean. It is probably this double function which first brought man and dog together. Certainly by the Mesolithic, some fifteen thousand years ago, if not earlier, man had already domesticated the dog.

Agriculture

Agriculture, the domestication or cultivation of plants for the purpose of human consumption, was probably independently discovered by different human groups at different times in different parts of the world. The discovery more often than not was probably made by women, for the simple reason that women are everywhere the foragers, the food-gatherers, the seekers of roots and seeds, and presumably had better opportunities for observing the relation between dropped seeds and their germination. Women were probably the first gardeners and agriculturalists. Planting, weeding, and harvesting is still a woman's job in most nonliterate societies. It is only when agriculture displaces hunting as an economic activity and becomes a major job that men take over.

The earliest evidence we have of the domestication of plants is from a people who occupied the Mount Carmel caves in the Wadi-en-Natuf in Palestine. The Natufians date back to about 7000 B.C., and they appear to have occupied their caves till about 5000 B.C. The importance of the Natufians for us lies in the fact that among their implements were found the earliest known examples of agricultural implements, namely, sickles. These consisted of toothed-flint sickle blades set in a row into bone or antler handles. The sickle blades are characterized by a high polish such as that derived from the silica contained in the stems of cereal plants. While we have no direct evidence that the Natufians actually harvested cereal plants in this way, the probabilities are high that they did so. Although it is unnecessary to sickle wild cereals since upon ripening the heads automatically burst open and scatter the seed (the best way to gather such grain is by rubbing the heads between the palms of the hands or by striking them with a stick so that the grain

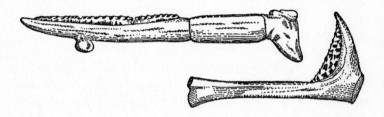

FIG. 30 *Natufian bone sickles*

falls into a receptacle), the mutant cereal plants are of the non-scattering variety and have to be sickled, then threshed at leisure. If they were not so treated they would rot, and since the heads would not automatically open, they would not reproduce themselves. Hence, it seems highly probable that they must have been artificially opened and the seed planted by man.

The Natufians had no domestic animals other than the dog and were without pottery, though they made stone vessels. Mortars and pestles of stone suggest that they ground the cereals they almost certainly cultivated.

The earliest agricultural settlement known in which there is direct evidence of plant cultivation has been excavated at Jarmo in the foothills of southern Kurdistan in northeastern Iraq. Here two-row barley and emmer wheat were recovered, as well as sickles, mortars and pestles, and weighted digging sticks. Here, too, there was no pottery, but stone vessels had been made, as well as adz- and ax-blades sharpened by grinding. Small flint implements known as microliths, were found here as among the Natufians. The villagers of Jarmo lived in mud-walled houses and bred stock animals such as goats, sheep, pigs, and cattle—the earliest evidence of domesticated animals, the very same animals that form the basic stock animals to this day. The Jarmo settlement dates back to about 5000 B.C. The Natufians were a Mesolithic folk. The Jarmo villagers made progress from the Mesolithic toward the Neolithic but did not altogether attain a Neolithic culture.

Mount Carmel in Palestine and Jarmo in Kurdistan are both situated within the region known as "the Fertile Crescent," that vast semicircle of land that fringes the great deserts from Palestine to the Persian Gulf. To the north lie the foothills of Kurdistan, through which the turbulent Tigris and Euphrates run their course, one for fifteen hundred and the other for seventeen hundred miles, emptying into the Persian Gulf. In this region conditions were especially favorable for the development of agriculture and the first permanent settlements.

By about 4000 B.C. some of the peoples of Lower and Middle Egypt, such as the Tasians, the Badarians, the Merimdeans, and the Faiyumis, had made the passage into the New Stone age or Neolithic, the age characterized by the first polished-stone and ground-edged implements, by the domestication of animals, by agriculture, and by the making of pottery. The Tasians lived mainly by hunting and fishing and were nomadic or seminomadic, but they had pottery and ground-stone axes, and used rubbing stones for grinding small grains like wheat or barley. The Tasians occupied a settlement at Tasa near the east bank of the Nile in Middle Egypt.

The Merimdeans of Merimde Beni Sālame, a settlement on the desert margin of the western edge of the Nile Delta, lived in wood-framed huts in stockaded villages, kept cattle, sheep, and goats, and cultivated cereals. The Faiyumis, who lived beside a great lake (now desert) in the Faiyum in Lower Egypt, also kept pigs. They hunted and fished and cultivated wheat and barley, which, like the Merimdeans, they gathered with sickles and stored in large pits lined with straw matting. The bow and arrow appears to have been the chief hunting implement.

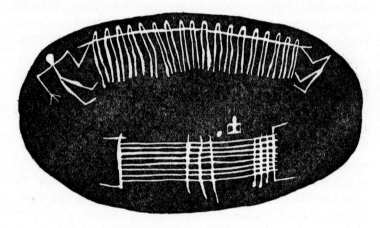

FIG. 31   *Loom depicted on early Egyptian pottery dish*

These three people, the Tasians, the Merimdeans, and the Faiyumis, were Stone Age people, but the Badarians, who followed them, learned how to hammer copper, although they never discovered how to melt, smelt, or mold it.

The pottery of these peoples we owe, no doubt, to the increase in leisure which the cultivation of plants and the domestication of animals first made possible. Textiles were woven out of flax, other vegetable fibers, and wool, baskets out of reeds, and bags from various fibers. The earliest representation of a loom is found on a pottery dish discovered in a woman's tomb at Badari dating as far back as 4400 B.C.

The Badarians were followed by the Amratians whose appearance marks the beginning of the predynastic period in Egypt and dates back to a little over 4000 B.C. The Amratians were culturally much like the Badarians, but in addition made use of alphabetlike signs—though not in a manner that could be called writing.

Another culture that succeeded the Badarian, that of the Gerzeans, who lived somewhat west of the Faiyum, reached a high order of technical perfection in many respects. Its pressure-flaked implements are among the most beautiful of their kind. Copper, lead, and silver were known, and olives, in addition to cereals, were cultivated. The rudiments of a script based on older Paleolithic hunting signs were in use, and the Gerzeans played a game resembling checkers. For the first time in the history of man, as far as we know, a king makes his appearance. It is believed that it was the Gerzeans who invented the calendar as an aid to agriculture, in order to foretell the date of the annual inundation of the Nile.

Following the Gerzean culture, there is a steady development in civilization: the overgrown villages become autonomous towns with their own officials; the use of copper and other metals becomes more frequent; the potter's wheel is discovered; and with the regular use of writing, history begins.

Stock-Breeding and Pastoralism

It is interesting to note that the earliest domestication of animals should have taken place at approximately the same time as the cultivation of cereals. The principle underlying the two forms of food production are the same: the control of reproduction. As we have already mentioned, the earliest animals to be domesticated for the purposes of food are those we still use, cattle, sheep, goats and pigs. Their bones are found

in the earliest agricultural settlements of Jarmo in Kurdistan
and in the settlements of the Faiyumis, Merimdeans, and
Badarians in Neolithic Egypt. That the horse was used as a
domestic animal in Elam, at the head of the Persian Gulf,
earlier than 3500 B.C., is known from a representation of a
man riding one. From Sumerian art of about 3000 B.C. we
know that the wheeled cart was invented with horses and cattle
as draft animals.

Pastoral communities, living largely off their herds, were
well established by 4000 B.C., and there are many peoples today in Mongolia and Arabia who still follow this mode of subsistence, as do the Navahos of our own Southwest.

Personal Care and Dress

Judging from existing nonliterate peoples, attention to the
cleanliness of one's body and to one's appearance in general is
universally distributed. In the latter case it is principally the
females, rather than the males, who excel, apparently because
males everywhere place a high value upon physically attractive
females.

It is an error to suppose that clothing is usually worn for
protective purposes; in nonliterate societies it is worn mainly
for decorative purposes. In most nonliterate societies, before
the influence of the clothed white man, only such clothing was
worn as was thought desirable, and what was thought desirable varied from society to society. In some societies it was
considered immodest to expose certain parts of the body; in
other societies complete nudity was the rule, as among the
Australian aborigines and many African peoples. The Onas of
Tierra del Fuego live in perhaps the worst climate in the
world, a climate of bitter cold, snow and sleet, and heavy rains
a great deal of the time, yet they usually remain entirely naked.

During extremely cold weather they may wear a loose cape of fur and rub their bodies with grease. The Australian aborigines live in a climate of daily extremes. During the day the temperature may be 120 degrees in the shade; at night it may fall below freezing! Yet they wear no clothes at all. At night the aboriginal builds a small fire and curls himself around it, waking every so often to put on a few more twigs in order to keep the fire burning.

Among the American Indians of earlier times everything from tailored clothes to complete nudity could be found. The Indians in the vicinity of San Francisco Bay resorted to coats of mud to keep themselves warm. The Athapascan-speaking Indians of the Mackenzie River still make their garments of tanned hides. Eskimos, during the winter months of the year, are forced to clothe themselves in the warm furry skins of the animals they hunt. Their clothing is, in fact, a masterpiece of ingenuity.

Clothing in some societies is used to symbolize differences in social status. Only great warriors could wear the feather bonnet that has come to be associated with the Plains Indians. Large ear ornaments could be worn only by the ruling classes among the Incas, and only certain classes were permitted to wear certain feather-decorated garments. In our society a hospital doctor wears a doctor's coat, a working man frequently wears overalls, a nurse wears a nurse's uniform, and there are the various other kinds of distinguishing clothes—soldiers' and sailors' uniforms, the royal ermine of the reigning house, and the like. Clothing is clearly not to be explained in terms of biological needs alone, for it serves many psychological and social purposes.

Evidence of the first clothing comes from the Neolithic of France, but it is almost certainly much older than that. In the Aurignacian period we find needles made of bone, as we do in the later Solutrean and Magdalenian periods. These were undoubtedly used in the sewing of garments. Since Neanderthal man lived during part of the Würm glaciation, he undoubtedly wore some form of clothing to protect himself against the cold.

Shelter

The gorilla makes use of rock ledges from time to time, and many of the remains of prehistoric men have been recovered from caves. *Sinanthropus* (Peking man) is the earliest form of man that we know lived in caves. Cave dwellers usually lived just inside the mouth of the cave, because they could have a fire burning a good deal of the time at the mouth, whereas in the interior it would smoke everyone out. It may come as a surprise to you to learn that at the present time human beings, in millions, are still living in caves. And not just in Mongolia or Arabia, but in Europe. At the present time there are over a million people in Spain alone who make their permanent home, as their ancestors have before them, in caves!

Where there are no caves, every people builds some form of shelter for protection, depending upon the available materials and the need. Nomads build impermanent shelters; sedentary peoples build substantial ones. But there are always exceptions. The Polar Eskimos are nomadic, but they build permanent houses of stone, to which they return after the summer's wanderings. The snowhouse, or igloo, is used only as a temporary shelter which one readily abandons. A movable tent of hide serves a similar purpose during the summer hunting season. The Onas of Tierra del Fuego, in an extremely rainy and cold climate, build only simple windbreaks of guanaco skins supported by poles to protect them from the weather. The Australian aboriginal builds a similar windbreak made of twigs and leaves, but on occasion he will erect a more substantial hut, of the simplest kind, of wood and grass. The Plains Indians, nomadic hunters, used the tepee, a skin tent which was easily moved. The Crow Indians erected a tepee made of many buffalo skins sewn together which was twenty-five feet high and could accommodate more than twenty people.

An elaborate portable shelter is the *yurt*, made by the Kazak of central Asia. This consists of a light wooden framework covered with felt. Some yurts have wooden doors and are separated into several rooms; the floor is beaten earth covered with rugs. The yurt is usually transported by oxen, horses, or camels, and can be erected in a half-hour.

Clearly, the type of house or shelter a people erects will depend upon a number of factors, principally on the state of their technological development and only secondarily on their environment. The British Columbian fishing Indians, who built large, elaborate houses of wood that were permanent and immovable, are a special case since they were able to store enough food after the salmon run to last them a year and so were able to lead the life of wealthy "farmers."

The Iroquois of the eastern woodlands built "long houses," which were communal dwellings, rectangular in shape, some 20 to 30 feet in width, about 50 to 150 feet in length, and about 20 to 30 feet in height. From a central corridor running the full length, separate apartments opened on each side. Built of bark, long houses were substantial structures.

The Pueblo structures of New Mexico and Arizona are houses built of stone laid in adobe mortar or of adobe clay bricks that have been dried in the sun. The roofs, also of stone or adobe, are supported by log beams. These houses are communal dwellings, the separate apartments being built in stepped tiers four or five stories high. The skyscraper stone buildings of Lhasa, Tibet, were built long before our own.

Whether hut or duplex apartment, a house is something

more than a shelter. It is also a place where the family can be together, and where together and alone, they can enjoy a certain amount of privacy. However gregarious a person may be, there are many times during his life when he enjoys the pleasures of solitude—absolute or relative. The privacy of the house affords the family and the individual an opportunity for reflection and careful planning.

Weapons

There is no evidence of the manufacture of weapons as instruments of offense or defense against other men until the Neolithic. When tribes began to cultivate herds of livestock, raids began to occur. In order to protect property against marauders, defenses were erected, and new and more weapons manufactured. Sometimes a marauder was captured, leading to the discovery that instead of killing the enemy one could enslave him. Thus was slavery born, in the Neolithic of what is now the Middle East.

A Neolithic raid may not have been comparable to a Second World War, but it was war nonetheless. After the horse was introduced into America, raiding for horses became a common practice among the Plains Indians, but the attempt was usually made without any desire to harm the owners of the horses. Often as many as a hundred horses would be taken by the raiding parties, as well as mules and cattle. Not infrequently these raiding parties would result in bloody conflicts.

In the Neolithic the increase in the number of weapons found—battle-axes, rapiers and swords of bronze or iron—suggests that either individuals or groups or both had made the sorry discovery that by acquiring the property of one's neighbor, one could increase one's own wealth, that war, in fact, was an economically productive activity—a totally erroneous belief which has bedeviled men down to the present day. It was in the Neolithic that man started off on the wrong foot with the discovery that the acquisition of large amounts of property leads to power, and that when one has power the only thing remaining to achieve is—more power. Food-gatherers and simple cultivators don't seem to think this way —they are too busy making a living—but pastoral peoples and mixed farmers seem to hanker after the acquisition of cattle and of slaves. Nonliterate people like the Australian aborigines and the Eskimos do not engage in warlike activities at all. In fact, it is extremely difficult to make them understand that there exist peoples on the earth who engage in such activities.

The raiding of American Indians is to be regarded as a form of warfare, but the head-hunting activities of New Guinea natives, and until recently the Dayaks of Borneo, are not properly so regarded. The motivation in such cases is not really infliction of injury upon another tribe in order to obtain its property, but rather to obtain for ritual purposes a magical increase in strength.

Weapons have been made of every conceivable material, from wood to tempered steel, and doubtless every possible peaceful implement that could be used for the purposes of war has been so used. Since wood is perishable, we know very little concerning its uses as material for weapons, but from the bone and stone points which have been recovered by the thousands, it is clear that in many cases they were associated with a wooden handle or shaft. Sling stones, used as ammunition, found in Iran date back to about 4500 B.C., mace-heads have been found at Merimde, and battle-axes become abundant during the Bronze Age (1500 B.C.).

Though some peoples, like the raiding Indians we have already discussed, certainly raided in order to acquire the property of their neighbors, Australian aborigines will take revenge

on a member of another tribe for wife-stealing or for a pre-
vious killing of one of their own folk. Polynesians have attacked
another group in order to obtain a victim for sacrificial killing,
and so have the Ashantis of Africa and the Aztecs of Central
America.

Occupations and Industries

Occupational differences came into being with human society itself. The division of labor between the sexes was the
first of these. Woman's work was of the domestic kind. In fact,
it might be said that in most nonliterate societies woman was
man's chief domesticated animal. Her work has always been
considered menial, that of a domestic servant. Man's work has
been of wider, and socially more esteemed, scope. It is only in
the most civilized societies that this grave error and injustice is
being gradually rectified. In many lands of the Western world,
the position of woman in society is being re-evaluated, especially the importance of her functions as a mother.

In Neolithic graves where one often finds dual burials of
husband and wife, the wife is usually much younger than the
husband. Wives were probably buried alive with their husbands as a rule, but sometimes, as we know from the arrow-
heads found in their bones and around the skeleton, they were
killed before the burial.

It has already been stated that women, as the gatherers of
plant foods, which they are in every hunting and food-gathering society at the present day, were the inventors of horticul-
ture and probably also of agriculture. The Neolithic revolution
was therefore the creation of women, its development the
work of both men and women. But we may be certain that the
raiding activities which came in the Late Neolithic were the
work of men. It will be the task of women to reteach men
how to conserve rather than to destroy.

In every nonliterate society there are medicine men, priests, elders of the council, skilled artists, skilled stone workers, skilled woodworkers, metal workers, educators, engineers, and so on. As society advances there is an increase in the differentiation of occupations until many of them become institutionalized in the form of guilds, educational institutions, and legal institutions. Institutions are collections of individuals who agree upon the performance of certain functions, with each individual still performing his occupational tasks separately, whether in medicine, law, the church, or education.

Industry came into being with human culture, and we have evidence of early industry in the form of the flint tools which early man made. It took great skill to manufacture these tools, and not everyone could make them. There is little doubt that in many early cultures gifted flint workers were employed as specialists, and possibly the latter trained other individuals to manufacture tools. It is also quite possible that flint workers taught other groups how to make tools in return for some consideration. We know that the teaching of art techniques was transmitted on bone or stone (see page 218), so that others many hundreds of miles away could benefit.

In the great riverine depressions of the Nile Valley, on the alluvial plains between the Tigris and the Euphrates, and on those in the vicinity of the Indus and its tributaries in Sind and the Punjab, the presence of a generous water supply made possible the production of food on a large scale. The digging of irrigation ditches and the draining of marshes rendered necessary the pooling of the labor of adjoining communities, and eventually the consolidation of social organization and the centralization of the economic system, with the accompanying centralizing of authority. Any men who had any ideas of cultivating their own plots, were now coerced to work under threat of having their water supply cut off. Large surpluses of foodstuffs could now be accumulated and traded in exchange for foreign goods. Specialized craftsmen had to be trained to work the foreign imports. Soldiers were needed to protect the transport of exports and imports, scribes to keep records of the transactions, and state officials to carry on the business of the State.

All this had already been developed in Mesopotamia, in Egypt, and in the Indus valley by 3000 B.C. It was in the Fertile Crescent, in the alluvial plains between the Tigris and the Euphrates, that the great second revolution in the history of humanity took place, the Urban Revolution, the growth of the city and of the city-state. It was here that the urbanization and the dehumanization of man began, with the control of human beings as commodities, while at the same time the development of the city made possible the development of all that we know as the good side of civilization. It is not the justness of a society's weights and measures which is the proper mark of its civilization, but its *kindness*. The overt expression of the inner civilization of a person is his kindness; the same is true of the community.

Transportation and Travel

If one moves from territory to territory, it is necessary to carry one's property with one. There are some nonliterate groups who have so little real property that they have a minimum of articles of transportation. The Australian aborigines, for example, make small net bags and a shallow wooden food-container, and nothing else. Other hunting peoples, such as the Eskimos, have built the most elaborate and ingenious transportation devices, of which the dog-drawn sled is the most remarkable. The Eskimos also use their dogs as pack animals as the Plains Indians used to do. The Peruvian Indians used the llama. Indeed, every possible animal has been put to this use by man—from dogs to elephants. The dog-drawn travois was a device used by the Plains Indians. Two poles were harnessed to the animal with the ends dragging on the ground, and the load was put on the platform that rested on the poles. In Central Asia, the same device is used drawn by a horse or some other animal.

The wheel was never discovered in America. It is first known from a representation in Sumerian art from about 3500 B.C. Interestingly enough, the wheel was not used in Egypt till about 1650 B.C. The wheel revolutionized transportation and accelerated communications enormously.

Thus far we have talked about transportation on land. Marine and river transport are no doubt very old. Navigable river-boats are known from Egypt from 4000 B.C., and these were undoubtedly sailboats. By 3000 B.C. such boats were sailing the eastern Mediterranean. Water transport is at least as old as the Mesolithic and was already well developed by the Neolithic.

Hewn-out trunks of trees and rafts are used by the Australian aborigines, and the Eskimos use that remarkable invention of theirs, the kayak, which they manipulate with consummate skill. The American Indian canoe is familiar to everyone. The outrigger canoe of Oceania is another remarkable invention of a nonliterate people. The outrigger was practically impossible to capsize, and it was possible to sail into the wind at an angle, an achievement unknown to Europeans before about the time of Columbus.

The most accomplished boatbuilders and sailors of the non-literate world were those remarkable people the Polynesians. Not only had they achieved great skill in boatbuilding, but their accomplishment was equally great in the science and art of navigation. This combination of qualities made them the most successful sailors the world has ever known, for they planned and achieved voyages by sea of two thousand miles and more. It is quite possible that on some of their voyages the Polynesians reached the coast of America.

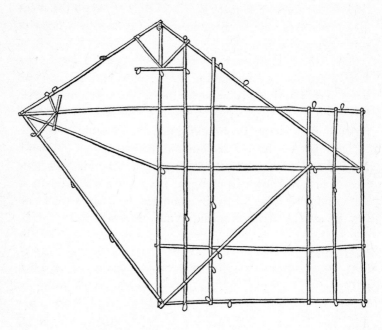

FIG. 32 *Polynesian navigation chart of tied sticks and shells*

Exchange of Goods and Services

Barter, trade, and commerce largely depend upon a society's exchangeable surpluses. On the other hand, one can on occasion manufacture something that one knows to be valued by a neighboring group. Aborigines of Northern Australia who possess a deposit of red ocher barter this with members of adjacent tribes for such things as weapons, fish, yams. The ocher is carried to its destination either in lumps or in a fine, prepared powder. It is used for decorating the body, as well as implements and weapons, and is everywhere much valued. Indeed, every Australian tribe seems to have engaged in some form of barter, and such activities were often associated with certain ceremonies. For example, upon the death of a male, members of the tribe sent their spears to neighboring tribes, who offered certain articles in exchange. These were then taken back by the original messengers and distributed among the owners of the spears. In this way, articles were obtained that were not manufactured within the tribe, and methods of making new implements were learned.

Barter is the direct exchange of goods for goods as such. Trade consists in the direct exchange of one value for another, either in terms of one another or some common denominator such as money. Commerce consists in the interchange of commodities and embraces both barter and trade.

The form of barter known as silent trade is very ancient and still widely practiced today. It consists in leaving a group of articles in a certain place and then going away. Later the other party arrives, examines the goods, and either leaves others in exchange or takes his departure without disturbing the original articles. The Congo pygmies and their Bantu neighbors so trade, as do the Reindeer Chukchees of Siberia with the maritime Chukchees. This practice was also followed by Californian Indians, and in Malaysia, New Guinea, and in other places.

Barter seems to be carried on more between tribes than within the tribe. Face-to-face trading is the common practice within nonliterate societies. In some societies some trade object is used as a common denominator of value. This is known as money-barter. In New Guinea and elsewhere cowrie shells may thus serve, in the Philippines rice, salt in West Africa, tobacco in Siberia, and metal objects in the Congo.

The use of money as such in nonliterate societies is pretty limited. It occurred in West Africa and the Congo, in Melanesia and western North America. Coined money first appears in the Late Bronze Age, the first coins having been minted by the Lydians of Greece about 700 B.C. Before that time, however, gold, silver, copper, and lead bearing impressed marks were in use as money in Assyria and Cappadocia some time between 2250 and 1200 B.C.

There is some evidence that cowrie shells were used as money in prehistoric times. In many Upper Paleolithic graves and those of Early Neolithic age, shells are associated with the body. Cowrie shells are found over wide areas of Europe, where they do not naturally occur, and hence must have traveled far from their original sources. This suggests that considerable value was placed upon these shells. It is, therefore, not improbable that they were used as a medium of exchange.

While money is a convenient technical device to facilitate the exchange of goods and services, it is also a fundamental factor in providing the driving force that stimulates the activities of all human society. Without money, civilization as we know it would have been impossible.

The compulsory acceptance of "gifts" is a form of trade practiced by the British Columbian Indians and some Melanesian peoples. The "gift" is made on the understanding that it will be repaid within a reasonable time. The Melanesians are great traders and make long journeys from island to island trading their goods in exchange for others. The profit motive is generally less involved than the prestige acquired in the process of trading.

Among the Zuñis of our Southwest, the emphasis is upon cooperation in all activities. The people live by agriculture and stock-raising. Many have automobiles. In all transactions within the tribe, there is a complete absence of the profit motive. Objects have no fixed exchange value, "sales" do not exist, property is simply transferred within the framework of personal relationships. In a singularly inhospitable physical environment where land is scarce, land has no value based on scarcity because, according to the Zuñis, what *is* scarce and expensive is the labor to work the land. When a field is "sold," the size and location is of less significance than the kinship ties and relative ages of those engaged in the transaction. "I bought this field" (a good cornfield), said one Zuñi, "for a piece of calico because he was an old man," meaning that the old man had no further use for the field. It is not without significance that the women among the Zuñis play the dominant role in economics.

Markets develop out of the periodic gatherings of neighboring groups for the exchange or sale of goods. Middlemen in nonliterate societies are quite frequent. Thus, the Wishram Indians, fishermen on the Columbia River, collected goods from as far as California and the Plains. At definite times they would hold markets where Indians could buy fish, slaves, canoes, shells, horses, and so on. The Auki villagers on Malaita Island in Melanesia manufacture shell money, which they trade for food at the markets that are regularly held on the island.

Markets are widely held throughout Africa and may go on for days. In the southwestern Congo the Bakubas hold markets every three days, and by this regular recurrence of the market they measure their week. In the Uganda the chiefs supervised the markets, fixed the price of commodities, and claimed a 10 per cent tax on all sales.

In the Aztec capital, Tenochtitlán, where Mexico City now stands, local markets were held daily in various parts of the city. In addition to barter, articles such as beans, cotton cloth, copper ax-blades, and quills of gold dust served as media of exchange. These articles had certain standardized values which were regulated by special officials, who also supervised weights and measures and adjudicated disputes.

In addition to the immediate purposes achieved in the exchange of goods and services, trade has served to foster peaceful relations between peoples, to assist the spread of ideas and novel ways of doing things. Indeed, trade has been the great fertilizer, and the most complex civilizations have developed in those areas of the world which have been the great centers of trade.

Forms of Property

The American historian James Harvey Robinson said, "The little word *my* is the most important one in all human affairs and properly to reckon with it is the beginning of wisdom." The ownership of property entails the exclusive use, enjoyment, and control of those things which are of value. Property is personal when controlled by the individual, common when a number of individuals have rights in it.

Among hunting peoples generally, while property rights exist, they are often much less exclusive than among ourselves. A wife and children are one's exclusive property, but very little else among the Australian aborigines, the Eskimos, or the Bushmen of South Africa. Food is shared among the group according to certain definite rules, the best parts usually going to the oldest persons. Food stored in caches may be used by anyone. One owns tools and implements as long as one uses them. A house belongs to the family that built it only as long as that family continues to live in it.

Among most hunting peoples land is held in common, and hunting and food-gathering rights belong to all. There are generally no private rights of this kind. This was also true among the pastoral Hottentots of South Africa, but if a man dug a well or opened a spring, it was regarded as coming under his special authority, and, after inspection by the chief, was named after him. Anyone wishing to use the water had to obtain special permission from him, but it was equally his duty to see that no stranger nor his stock was denied access to it.

The Hopi Indians, a horticultural people, own the land in common, title being vested in the clan, an enlarged family, and the land being distributed among the clan members for their use. As among the Eskimos, houses, tools, and other artifacts are owned by those who make them and use them. The right to property is its possession; there is no ownership which is not accompanied by use, and consequently no wealth which enables an individual to live off of the labor of his fellows.

In nonliterate societies generally, the tribe is but an overgrown family rather than a State. Kinship ties and ceremonials hold it together, everyone is more or less related to everyone else, and the line of descent determines inheritance and social position. The compulsion of blood renders the terms "private" and "public" quite inappropriate. Common ownership is understandable under these conditions, with, of course, the usual rights of the individual to what he happens to have and is using. The mark of property becomes most manifest in intertribal relations. The tribe lays claim to its own hunting grounds, its real property, and also to forms of incorporeal property such as songs, dances, incantations, and gods. Incorporeal property rights have been, however, often vested in individuals who held the exclusive rights to certain chants or songs, myths, designs, poems, and the like. Usually no one ventured to indulge in any of these activities without special permission from the owner. An Andaman Islander, a Plains Indian, a Melanesian, and a Chukchee never ventured to sing the song of another without permission. There is often a divine sanction to the rights in a song or chant or dance, and this may be one reason why the right is so rigidly respected.

Those who know special incantations own a valuable property which, as among the Siberian Koryaks, they often sell at a good price. A vision that has been revealed to one, among the Plains Indians, for example, is so strictly one's own property that it cannot be transferred even to one's son without a formal sale. In matrilineal Melanesian tribes, however, it was obligatory to teach one's sister's son the magic spells.

Among the California Indians and some of the other simpler nonliterate societies, material property was not inherited, but destroyed at death. The Onas of Tierra del Fuego wrap a dead man in whatever clothes he may possess and burn him, his hut, and all his belongings. His dogs may be turned over to some kinsman.

With the accumulation of property that is highly valued, there is reluctance to destroy it upon the death of the owner, and rules are devised to regulate the inheritance of such property. The fact that spouses are members of different kin groups usually prevents their inheriting from each other. The individual, in nonliterate societies rarely has the freedom to will his property to whomever he wishes—the social rules take care of that. In some societies inheritance passes through the female line, and these are known as *matrilineal*; when descent is reckoned in the male line it is known as *patrilineal*. This does not mean that in the first case males get nothing (or that in the second females get nothing), but rather that the disposition of most of the property is in the hands of the females (or in those of the males).

We perceive, then, that the institution of private property is nowhere absent, but that it may be restricted to special things. The more advanced the society is, the more exclusive property rights tend to be. The conception of property rights prevailing in any society reflects the social and political structure of the society, and reacts upon those structures to create prestige, classes, and political power.

10

Sex and Marriage Patterns

E VERY SOCIETY makes certain basic distinctions that are based on the facts of nature, the two primary facts being sex and age. On the basis of sex, children are trained in particular ways, learning what others expect from them and what they may expect from others. This socialization process, as it is called, everywhere differs for the sexes.

The division of labor has already been discussed, but there are many other qualities which are inculcated in the sexes that are, in each culture, considered feminine virtues on the one hand and masculine ones on the other. Much of the differentiation between the sexes that was formerly taken to be biologically determined we now know to be culturally determined, determined not by nature but by nurture. In the Western world, particularly, we observe women daily performing tasks which only a few generations ago were pretty widely considered beyond their capacities. With the increasing freedom granted to women, there has been a noticeable decline in the frequency of swooning and the "vapors," which seemed to be peculiar to the gentler sex in the Victorian period. There is scarcely an occupation that women in the civilized regions of the world do not fill, and fill most efficiently.

In most nonliterate societies women are certainly regarded as the inferior sex and are less valued than men. The male by virtue of his greater muscular power is able to enforce his social superiority by brawn whenever it is challenged by the female, which is seldom indeed. Women have been forced to develop tactical approaches to the male of an indirect kind. Hence, in all societies in which women are dealt with primitively (and this does not yet exclude our own society), women are alleged to possess greater cunning and shrewdness, to be more selfish, and more concerned with sex than the male. These traits are all culturally produced. Where women appear to be more concerned with sex than males, it is principally because the males expect the females to make themselves attractive. In fact, it is often necessary for females to compete with one another for the scarcer male's attention. It is evident that in almost all societies the male is more preoccupied with sex than the female.

Sexual Behavior

In almost all nonliterate societies premarital sexual freedom is more widely permissive than it is in more complex societies. This freedom is considered to be an educational preparation for marriage, and in many societies, as among the Muria tribe of India, such behavior is encouraged by the provision of definite boys' and girls' houses where each may take temporary partners.

In nonliterate societies there are generally no hard and fast rules concerning the number of wives a man may have; he may generally have as many as he can afford. Having more than one wife is an economic advantage, but the difficulty of obtaining even one wife in such a society as that of the Australian aborigines is often very great, and there are few men who have more than one wife in Australian aboriginal societies. There are some societies, such as the Todas of southern India, in which one woman may have many husbands. This form of union is known as *polyandry*, the union in which a man may have more than one wife is known as *polygyny*, both states are covered by the term *polygamy*, and marriage of only two persons is known as *monogamy*. Most nonliterate peoples actually live in monogamous unions.

Marriage

Marriage, the legal union of a man with a woman, is distinguished from mating, the temporary union of males and females, for marriage is a socially sanctioned union entered into with the assumption of permanency. Everywhere the function of marriage is to provide a socially sanctioned, stable background for the mating of husband and wife so that they may produce and raise children. Indeed, marriage is the principal institution designed to insure the continuation of the family and other groupings based on kinship.

In most nonliterate societies marriage is not a matter which is left to chance, as it is in most of our modern civilized societies, but is more or less strictly regulated within a definite framework. In all societies there is a proscription against marrying parents and brother and sisters, and this is sometimes extended to cousins. There are, however, exceptions. For example, the kings of ancient Egypt had so hypertrophied a sense of their own importance that they felt that there was no one good enough, that is, of sufficiently pure "blood" to marry, so they married their own sisters. In fact, seven pharaohs, one after the other, did so, and it should be recorded that their offspring appear to have been of outstanding ability and intelligence. For the same reason such unions were favored by Peruvian and Hawaiian royalty. This suggests that the horror of incest is not inborn but a distaste which is acquired.

In many societies all marriages must be made with members of other tribes outside one's own group. Such marriage practices are known by the name of *exogamy*; marriage within one's own group is called *endogamy*. The origin of the incest prohibition has puzzled anthropologists for many years, and there have been many theories. The most widely accepted is that incest was an artificially created dislike designed to encourage marriages outside the group. It is assumed that the prohibition is very ancient, and that what it was designed to achieve was to place members of one's own group in that of a neighboring group to act as ambassadors. Similarly, members of the other group performed the same function, and thus good relations were maintained between groups. It must be said that this is a conjecture. We shall probably never be able to ascertain the origin of the incest prohibition.

Among some nonliterate peoples a bond of kinship is believed to exist between members of the same clan or even sections of the same clan, and therefore marriage between such members comes under the incest ban while marriage outside one's own particular social group is encouraged. Finally, it should be obvious that incest prohibitions secure the marriage of members of different families with one another, thus knitting two families into a larger cooperating group.

Preferential Marriage

In all societies the individual is responsible to his social group. In general the family constitutes the agent of the larger community, and it is through it that the behavior of the individual tends to be regulated. Marriage is one of the forms of behavior which tends to be very carefully regulated in all societies since marriage involves the creation of close ties not only between the marrying individuals, but also between their families. In marriage, kinship is established between two groups, not merely between two individuals. It may readily be understood, then, why each group should feel itself deeply involved in the marriage of any of its members. In our own society, parents and other relatives often see to it that marriages are contracted between their children and those of other parents who have had a similar background, or belong to the same "race," or ethnic group, or socioeconomic group, or religion. Most Catholics tend to marry members of their own religious faith; to that extent they practice a form of endogamy. Jews are similarly likely to marry members of their own faith.

In numerous societies, cross-cousin marriage is obligatory. The term "cross-cousin" refers to cousins whose parents are brother and sister. If you are a male, then your cross-cousin is your mother's brother's daughter. If you are a female, your cross-cousin is your father's sister's son. Your father's brother, whether you are male or female, is your parallel uncle; your mother's sister is your parallel aunt. But your mother's brother is a cross-uncle and your father's sister a cross-aunt. Parallel and cross-uncles and aunts are equally close relatives, yet a very large number of societies regard parallel kin as closer. Parallel uncles and aunts are frequently called "father" and "mother," and they in turn call their nephews and nieces "son" and "daughter," other terms being used for cross-relatives. The children of parallel uncles and aunts are often called "brothers" and "sisters" by their cousins, and since they are regarded as close "blood" relatives, marriage between them is considered incestuous and therefore forbidden.

In still other societies (the Miwoks of California and the

Murngins of Australia), one may marry the daughter only of one's maternal uncle, but not the daughter of one's paternal aunt. In the Trobriand Islands precisely the reverse rule obtains. Such forms of marriage are known as asymmetrical cross-cousin marriages.

Parallel-cousin marriage often takes the form of marriage of a male with his father's brother's daughter, as among the Bedouin Arabs of northern Arabia. This serves to keep the males within the band, and thus preserve a strong defensive and fighting force.

In many societies, upon marriage the wife is required to go and live in her husband's village. This is known as *patrilocal* or *virilocal* residence; the opposite condition in which the married couple settles in the domicile of the wife's family is known as *matrilocal* or *uxorilocal* residence.

The forms of marriage known as the *levirate* (Latin: *levir*, brother-in-law) and *sororate* (Latin: *soror*, sister) are very widely distributed. The levirate is the practice of marrying one's brother's—usually older brother's—widow. The sororate is the practice of marrying a younger sister of one's dead wife. The levirate was practiced among the ancient Jews, as the Old Testament tells us, and it is well distributed among nonliterate peoples. Among the Chiricahua Apaches of North America both the levirate and sororate are practiced. Both the levirate and sororate may be obligatory, preferential, or permissive in different societies. The function of the levirate and the sororate is to maintain the bonds originally established between the two families, to ensure that they are not dissolved by death.

In many Indian tribes a man established a legal title, upon marriage, to his wife's sisters and kinswomen, and upon their attaining maturity he could consummate marriage with them —a custom known as *sororal polygyny*.

In some American Indian tribes, such as the Shoshone Indians of Idaho, and among the Australians and the Melanesians, *interfraternal* or *interfamilial exchange marriage* occurred. This involves a brother and sister of one family marrying a sister and brother of another family. "Take thou my sister and give me thy sister" was the formula used by the Arab people of Artas (Palestine).

Marriage by Capture

In Europe, the Yugoslavs, Orthodox as well as Roman Catholic, practiced forcible capture of girls for the purpose of marriage well into the nineteenth century. This often resulted in bloodshed. The Plains Indians often obtained wives in this way, and until recently many such wives were still living among the remnants of our Plains Indians. Such wives enjoyed all the privileges of other wives.

Mock capture is practiced in many tribes, and this is, of course, by common agreement. It is found widely spread throughout Africa, and occurs in Melanesia and in China. Where females are scarce groom capture may be practiced, as among the Kambots of New Guinea.

Marriage by Service

In Genesis 29:18 Jacob says to his mother's brother, Laban: "I will serve thee seven years for Rachel thy younger daughter." But he was given the older daughter, Leah, instead, because the firstborn had to be given before the younger. So Jacob did a stretch of another seven years for Rachel.

Marriage by service is generally associated with matrilocal residence. This form of marriage is .the regular practice among the Siberian Chukchee, Koryak, and Yukaghir tribes, among the North American Winnebago and Hidatsa Indians, and the loosely organized tribes of the Chaco.

In many tribes marriage by service is regarded as a substitute or alternative for the regular form of marriage.

Bride Purchase

In nonliterate societies the most usual way of obtaining a wife is by purchase. This does not mean that one buys a wife as one buys a mat or any other object. A purchaser of an object usually retains absolute rights to it. Not so in the case of bride purchase or wife purchase. A man cannot intemperately abuse his wife without calling forth the wrath of his in-laws and, often, of his society. Husbands cannot sell their wives, even though they may otherwise dispose of their services.

While the payment for the bride may in part be regarded as a recompense to the family for the loss of her services, it is usually much more than that. The amount paid often determines the prestige that the bride will enjoy in her spouse's and in her own community. The purchase price endows the bride with a certain value. If the price is high, she thereby becomes a person not to be too lightly valued. The dowry that those of European descent provide for their daughters serves much the same function. In the latter case the husband gains the advantage, which he is expected to share with his wife; among nonliterate peoples it is the bride's family that gains the advantage. Marriage by bride purchase tends to be associated with patrilocal residence.

Inheritance of Wives

In some societies a son may inherit all his father's wives, with the exception of his own mother, upon the death of the father. This is known as *filial widow inheritance*. It was practiced among the medieval Mongols, as reported by Marco Polo, and also by the Araucanians of Chile. Among the Palvic and Bura tribes of Northern Nigeria, a grandson could inherit his grandfather's wives.

Group Marriage

Marital union between several men and several women is known as group marriage. Such marriage is actually known to occur in but a single tribe, the Kaingang of Brazil. Even among the Kaingang only 8 per cent of all recorded marriages were of the group variety, as compared with 14 per cent polyandrous, 18 per cent polygynous, and 60 per cent monogamous. As one may correctly gather from these statistics, the Kaingang have exceedingly flexible attitudes toward their sexual associations.

Elopement

Runaway matches have probably occurred in all societies, and in some it is the usual way of getting married. Among the Kurnais of southeastern Australia ten or a dozen couples eloped at a time. The older people tended to wink at these elopements, but, often enough, a father was very angry, even though he had himself married in the same way. With the passage of a little time, however, the eloped couple was readmitted into the tribe, perhaps first having to undergo a formal beating.

Adoptive Marriage

In Indonesia and Japan a man may obtain a wife by being adopted into the family. By this means, a patrilineal family (one that reckons descent through the father) without sons secures its continuance. By a legal fiction, the son-in-law becomes a "son." The fact that his wife thereby becomes his sister is conveniently overlooked.

Whatever form of marriage we consider, the function of marriage is everywhere the same: to cement the bonds of society through the cementing of the bonds between a male and a female, who, in their reciprocal relationship, will combine both sexual and economic functions. By this means, through the family, the basis of society, the society will be maintained and controlled.

Divorce

Divorce is the dissolution of the marriage tie by competent authority. In most societies arrangements exist for the dissolution of marriage, and these are quite as various as the forms of marriage. In general, divorce is much less complicated among nonliterate than among literate peoples. There being neither religious nor governmental sanctions for marriage in the former societies, its dissolution is accomplished much more easily. The causes of divorce are many. In most nonliterate societies, adultery rarely constitutes cause for divorce, but where it is considered a cause, it is often punished. Barrenness is a frequent cause, and where a bride price has been paid, this is often returned to the husband or his family. Disease, laziness, and neglecting to provide food for the husband are widely encountered as causes for divorce. Among the Todas of southern India, there are only two reasons for divorce: one is that the wife is a fool, the other that she will not work. When a Toda man wants a divorce, he pays one buffalo to his wife's people, and in return he receives any buffalo he may have paid as the original bride price.

In general, divorce is no more difficult for women than it is for men in nonliterate societies, and in some societies women possess superior privileges in this respect. This is true among the Kwomas of New Guinea, the Dahomeans of West Africa, the Yurok Indians of California, and the Witoto of Brazil. Among the Arunta of Central Australia and the Baganda of East Africa, a man may divorce his wife at will, yet in neither society do women have the right of divorce. The Zuñi husband and wife have equal rights to divorce, but it is the woman who usually establishes it by merely depositing her husband's belongings outside the door. This was the case also among the Iroquois Indians of New York. Among the Chiricahua Apaches equal rights to divorce also obtain. It is interesting to note that in these three American Indian societies the status of women is quite high.

Divorce, like marriage, is a family affair, and in general families are inclined to discourage divorce, especially when the return of property is involved. On the whole, divorce is regarded as a regrettable necessity and a recognition of human frailty. In spite of the ease of divorce in nonliterate societies, it is by no means as frequent as might be supposed. Marriages are rarely entered into lightly, and the bonds established between husband and wife are not likely to be casually dissolved.

11

Family Patterns

THERE IS every reason to believe that the family, in the form of a more or less permanent union between a male and a female and their children, is the oldest of human institutions. In spite of nineteenth-century theories, it is now generally accepted that there never was a period in human evolution which was characterized by promiscuous relations between the sexes. The oldest of all human institutions, the family will continue to endure as the basic institution upon which society rests, no matter what social changes may develop. For a time, the Soviet Russians thought that they could eliminate the family, but they soon discovered how unworkable such an idea was.

The family is the social unit constituted by, yet distinguished from, marriage, which is the complex of customs which brings the family into being.

There are three kinds of family: (1) *The nuclear family*, consisting of a married man and woman with their children, is the kind of family that exists among ourselves. It is sometimes called the *conjugal* or *biological family.* The nuclear family is always *bilateral,* which means that each spouse is, through marriage, a member of two families. The children similarly are bilaterally related to their parents' families. (2) *The polygamous family* consists of two or more nuclear families affiliated by several marriages, that is, by having a single married parent in common. For example, under polyandry, one woman plays the role of wife and mother in several nuclear families and by so doing unites them into a larger familial group. Under polygyny, the more usual type of polygamous family, one man assumes this role. (3) *The extended family* consists of uncles, aunts, cousins, parents, grandparents, and grandchildren. Unilaterality in family relationships, where a child is considered to belong to the extended family of its father, is termed *patrilineal;* on the maternal side, the unilaterality is recognized by the term *matrilineal.*

Functions of the Family

The principal functions of the family are the following: (1) sexual, (2) economic, (3) reproductive, and (4), educational. In the family union the powerful sexual drive is creatively gratified, reproduction of the group is accomplished, the nuclear group taken care of, and the potentialities of the children for participation in their community brought to fruition.

In every society the parents are held responsible for the care and upbringing of their children. In matrilineal societies, such as those of the Trobriand Islanders and the Iroquois, the mother's brother will stand to the children as a father with respect to their education. Almost everywhere older children participate in the education of their younger siblings.

The Samoan Joint Family

In Samoa the unit of social and economic life is a household which consists of the members of a number of nuclear families joined together by patrilocal residence under the authority of a single headman (*matai*). A single household may consist of as many as fifty persons, all related to the headman by "blood," adoption, or marriage. The headman is treated with great respect, unless he is unworthy of it, and then he is likely to be deposed.

Ten or more households unite to form a village with the kinship bond as their principal tie. The headman with the highest title in the village is recognized as supreme chief. Theoretically the joint family headman holds the power of life and death over the members of the household, but this he is seldom called upon to use. In all things within the household, he is the supreme authority.

Very early in the life of the child, it is turned over to the care of its older brothers and sisters, who become entirely responsible for its care and discipline. By the time a child is six years of age, it has become an economic asset. At about their tenth year, brothers and sisters learn to become shy of one another, until they cease speaking to each other familiarly and avoid all contact with each other.

All the skilled, petty, and humdrum tasks of life that can be delegated to children are so delegated by their elders, including the tending of babies. Every child is at the beck and call of all its relatives, who have the right to demand its services and to criticize and interfere in its affairs. By the age of eight or nine, boys manage to escape this grind by following their fathers, and learning from them all that a boy should. Girls, however, cannot get away so easily. They can take out their first frustration in dancing, which they are encouraged to do, or they can escape from home for a time on the pretext of visiting relatives, with different groups of which they can live from time to time. In fact, rarely do most children live continuously in one household. Children may be given away to friends or relatives by formal adoption.

The Polar Eskimo Family

Life for the Polar Eskimos is very precarious. Populations are small, and the family is small, consisting of husband and wife and their children, and perhaps an older relative or two. The latter will be supported only as long as they are capable of contributing to the livelihood of the family, for unless they are able to do so they become a serious liability that may threaten the survival of the whole. This the older people are aware of, and they often beg to be abandoned and left to die. Their relatives are usually reluctant to do this, though they may be forced to. For the same reason, if children come too quickly, they are often exposed to die. If her husband dies, a young mother destroys her infant since it now has no means of support, and if the mother of a nursing baby dies, the baby is, for the same reason, buried with the mother, unless the father finds a woman in the community who can suckle the child.

This is not cruelty, but a regrettable necessity, for the Eskimos do not regard a baby as a complete human being until it is capable of sitting up. The Eskimos have the greatest love for their children. Mothers suckle their children for five years or even longer. No Eskimo child is ever corporeally punished —this is considered the greatest barbarism. Mothers instruct their daughters, and the fathers their sons, in the duties and privileges relating to their sex.

Practically everything that has been said of the Eskimos is true of the Australian aboriginal family. Among the Australian aborigines, much the same conditioning factors are operative to produce similar adjustments to an extremely inhospitable environment.

The nuclear structure of the Australian and Eskimo families, as well as that of the Bushmen of South Africa, is simple compared with the structure of the joint family of the Samoans or of the Chiricahua Apaches.

The Chiricahua Apache Family

Though the Chiricahua Apaches of the American Southwest are, like the Eskimos, the Australian aborigines, and the Bushmen, a hunting and food-gathering people, their land is a much more hospitable one than is that of any of the other three peoples. The populations of the Chiricahuas are therefore larger.

The household into which the child is born among the Chiricahuas is one of a cluster of families, each related unilaterally through the maternal line. Near an older woman and man live their unmarried sons and daughters, their married daughters and sons-in-law, their daughters' daughters (married and unmarried), and their daughters' unmarried sons. Upon marriage each daughter occupies a separate dwelling with her husband. Unmarried sons usually live in the parents' household, but unmarried adult sons may have their own adjoining dwelling.

The child develops its personality in relation to this large maternal extended family. Since the extended family from which the father has come may be located in the same vicinity, he may often see his paternal relatives, who invariably show a great deal of affection for him.

Discipline of the child is left to the parents who take their duties very seriously. Children are rarely chastised, though on occasion they are whipped if all other means fail, but the point is made that adults do not like to do this.

The extended family, typified here by the Chiricahuas, is very frequent among nonliterate peoples. In regions where a band of families can live together, it is most likely to occur, as among numerous African and American tribes.

The Clan

As a member of a family, one is bilaterally related to the families of both one's father and one's mother. Kinship is traced through both parents. There are some societies in which kinship is traced through only one parent, that is, unilaterally either through the paternal or maternal line. Such a unilateral kinship group is known as a *clan* (sometimes called a *sib,* and when reckoned through the male line, a *gens*). A patrilineal clan is one in which all the members (at least in theory) are descended from a single ancestor through males. A matrilineal clan is one in which all the members are descended from a single ancestress through females. A clan which consists of the members of a single ancestor is a *lineage.* Some clans consist of a single lineage, while others, as among the Hopi Indians, consist of several lineages. Clans are always exogamous, and therefore husband and wife belong to different clans. One is born into a clan and can never change it. One cannot voluntarily join a clan.

Families may die or dissolve, but the clan endures (in theory; in practice, in small populations, the clan frequently comes to an end because in a certain generation the children all belong to the sex that does not transmit the name—in which case they attach themselves to another clan and are adopted by it as real members). Certainly the clan appears to be more stable than the family in many nonliterate societies. If there are no siblings in one's family, one has siblings in one's clan. The clan serves as an auxiliary family, and no matter how remote clan members may be from one another in space, their kinship, as well as the duties and privileges that go with it, constitutes an indissoluble bond between them. Clan members are always expected to help each other, and in any issue they stand together against all other clans. Sometimes members of one clan are hostile to members of another clan, as among the Witoto of the Amazon, and in their own self-interest they may be opposed to the welfare of the group as a whole.

Clans do not appear until societies have advanced beyond the earliest stages of complexity, and they tend to disappear with the development of strong centralized governments.

Moieties

When two intermarrying clans dwell together, each is called a *moiety*. Moieties may be exogamous, agamous (not regulating marriage), and endogamous. Exogamous moieties are common in Australia, less so in North America, and virtually entirely wanting in Africa. The Canella and the Cayapo tribes of Brazil are characterized by the presence of agamous clans or moieties.

In societies in which there are many clans, the clans are regarded as subdivisions of the moieties. Among the Seneca Indians, for example, there are two moieties, one consisting of the Bear, Wolf, Turtle, and Beaver clans and the other of the Deer, Snipe, Heron, and Hawk clans. Marriages were originally between members of the clans belonging to different moieties.

Phratries

Where several clans consider themselves especially bound to each other and not as closely bound to other clans, they are, as a group, called a *phratry* (Greek: *phratēr,* brother). Subdivided moieties may be phratries, but a phratry need not be a moiety. It is simply a union between two or more clans. A tribe may have moieties and phratries.

The splitting of big groups into little groups, and these in turn into littler groups, is a tendency that operates in all human associations. But the reverse process is at least as strong, and it is undoubtedly the one that has been operative to the largest extent in the making of human societies. The family came first, and society developed out of the family.

The Functions of the Clan

The functions of the clan are primarily: (1) to provide a bond of solidarity through the belief in their common descent, (2) to provide its members with all the necessary protections that they might otherwise be unable to secure, (3) to regulate and control marriage, (4) to adjudicate in disputes; and secondarily to provide the following sanctions for its members: (1) governmental, (2) economic, (3) religious and ceremonial, and (4) totemic.

The clan does not always function to the advantage of the society as a whole, and as society progresses, the functions of the clan are gradually taken over by the state.

Methods of Reckoning Relationship—Kinship

When a child is born to a married couple there are at once established a number of definite relationships to various persons on both the mother's and father's side. In our society these relationships are restricted to the members of one's own family and the families of one's parents. While we emphasize blood relationships and relationships established by marriage, nonliterate societies emphasize the *generation*. When we say "father," "mother," "son," and "daughter," as well as "brother" and "sister," we know that these are all relatives of the first degree; they are immediate "blood" relatives. In nonliterate societies such immediate relationships are subordinated, and the notion of the generation to which one is related is elevated into what anthropologists call the *classificatory system*. In the classificatory system kinship is determined by affinity as well as by consanguinity.

A member of the Arunta of Central Australia, for example, uses the term "father" to designate his own father, his father's brother, his father's first cousin, and so on. All relatives in each generation are grouped into four categories. Everyone in the grandparental generation is either (1) *arunga,* father's father or his sister, (2) *apulla,* father's mother or her brother, (3) *chimmia,* mother's father or his sister, or (4) *ipmunna,* mother's mother or her brother. Grandparents call grandchildren by the same terms that the latter call them.

As a matter of fact, the Australian aborigines in general do not distinguish between blood and marriage relationships. Among the Arunta and many other Australian tribes, relationships are primarily social rather than biological. For example, the mother's husband is considered the father of a child no matter who the actual genitor may have been. It is sociological paternity that is important, *not* biological paternity. The reason why illegitimacy is condemned is not that it is immoral, but that the child has no legal father and therefore cannot be properly incorporated into the society.

It would take us too far afield to consider other forms of

classificatory relationship here. The important thing is that every relationship system in nonliterate societies plays a very real and vital role in regulating the conduct of individuals toward each other, in determining what has been called kinship behavior.

Kinship Behavior

In all societies the relations between kin are established by custom. Parents stand in certain relations to their children, and children must behave in certain ways toward their parents. In many societies, brothers and sisters after a certain age must reduce and modify their familiar relations to each other. In some societies, where matrilineal descent is the rule, the mother's brother assumes many of the duties of the father, as among the Melanesian Trobrianders and the Haida of the Northwest Pacific Coast. The specific relation existing between a mother's brother and his sister's child is known as the *avunculate*. In Melanesia the father's sister oversees the choice of a boy's mate, and he is expected to respect his maternal aunt more than his own mother. This relationship is known as the *amitate*.

In-law avoidance behavior is widely prevalent in nonliterate societies. Such societies appear to have solved the mother-in-law problem by avoiding it. In a very large proportion of nonliterate societies, the son-in-law may not even look at his mother-in-law, and she may not even approach her son-in-law's hut. Among the Ona of Tierra del Fuego neither a man nor a woman may speak or even look at either of their parents-in-law. After a year the females may relax the prohibition on speech, but the prohibition remains absolute throughout the lives of the men.

Special privileged relationships in the form of *joking*

relatives are found among many peoples. In different cultures the privilege of teasing each other, indulging in violent practical jokes and horseplay at each other's expense, is enjoyed by sisters-in-law, brothers-in-law, cross-cousins, paternal grandfather and grandchild, a potential husband and the woman he may inherit, and so on. American Indian and Australian aboriginal peoples excel at this sort of thing. The explanation for such behavior offered by the anthropologists is that this privileged familiarity serves to compensate for the rather severe restraints which are put upon the behavior of most individuals within nonliterate societies as a consequence of the kinship systems.

12

Societal Controls and Government

I N THE PRECEDING PAGES we have considered something
of the social organization of nonliterate peoples. The social organization provides the framework upon which the individual can take his stand in relation to people. Every society has, in addition, developed means by which the behavior
of the individual is controlled, that is, regulated, checked, and
restrained. Under societal controls, mores and public opinion
are the two great regulative forces; under government, political forms and judicial and legal procedures serve similar
functions.

Mores

"Mores" (singular, "mos") may be understood to mean
the moral standards of a group, the customs or folkways that
are considered to contribute to group welfare. Every human
group has found that there are certain patterns of adjustment

to the environment (and the environment includes everything) which serve to make the wheels of society go round more smoothly, and these adjustments are incorporated into doctrines of group welfare. These doctrines are the mores of the group. By the standards which they set, they tell the individual, and the group, what behavior is right and what is wrong. The individual then knows what to do, and the society knows what to do when he doesn't do it. What may be considered immoral when the individual chooses to act on his own initiative, murder, for example, may become perfectly acceptable when society sanctions it as in war or in the execution of a criminal.

In nonliterate societies the acts of the individual are believed by everyone to have consequences for the group as a whole; hence, the individual tends to regulate his conduct by the recognition of his social responsibility to the group. Punishment for doing a wrong thing is likely to be immediate, not deferred to some afterlife. The individual is expected to be cooperative, altruistic, and noncompetitive; he is expected to be useful to his fellows and to respect them and contribute to their welfare. This view of human relations may or may not be extended to foreigners. In general, nonliterate people are very hospitable to men whom they have never seen before— after they have assured themselves that no harm is intended— but for tribes that are known to them, they may have great hostility and may even refuse to grant them the name of "men." Many tribes call themselves by names which mean in effect "we-are-men," implying that all others are not. This is the meaning that has sometimes been attributed to the name "Eskimo," but while it means "we-are-men," the Eskimos probably originally created it to distinguish themselves from animals; many of the Eskimos who were first visited by white men expressed extreme astonishment to find that there were

other men in the world, having been under the impression
that they were the only human beings in existence! James Ross
(1800–62), the great Scottish explorer, was so greeted by one
group of Eskimos who had never seen a white man before.

Among many nonliterate peoples it is the rule that terri-
torial and hunting rights are respected by neighboring tribes.
Anyone who breaks this rule is considered subject to death upon
sight. In this case it is not merely the fact that a member of
another tribe may be considered dangerous which will be the
cause of hostility toward him, but the fact that he has actually outraged a communal right.

All nonliterate societies expect children to pay attention
when addressed, but in some societies this is a matter of
morals, and the child learns very early, as in East Africa, that
respect for his elders is paramount. If he is wanting in respect
for his living ancestors, how can he be expected to respect
those who are dead?

Eskimos are among the most hospitable people in the world,
and stinginess, greed, and selfishness are regarded as most
reprehensible traits. When a man exhibits these to the extent
of becoming a menace to the group, if he does not improve
after having been given a chance to do so, he will be done
away with. The man's kin will not seek redress, for this was
an act committed in the interests of the group. But should an
Eskimo kill another man in a fight, a feud between the
families is precipitated, and atonement must be made.

Nonliterate societies place great emphasis on sharing as a
rule, and the selfish individual is generally condemned. Society is a cooperative venture, and the individual who does
not cooperate is behaving contrary to the interests of society.

Kindness to animals is a fairly universal trait among nonliterates, especially pastoral peoples. When, not so many years
ago, it was suggested to a Bantu chief that he yoke his oxen

to the plow and so improve his agriculture, he replied, "How can I be so cruel as to make them work?"

Kindness, indeed, is what morality is considered to be everywhere, and difficult as it may be for some to believe, kindness is what the law, at least ideally, also seeks to put into practice. Morality, in short, is the system of rules which gives significance to the activities of individuals in relation to each other.

Public Opinion

Public opinion is the expression of the moral judgment of a group. In the nonliterate groups moral judgment in action constitutes public opinion. The exhibition of an attitude, the inflection of a word, or a gesture may suffice to exert the proper effect. A similar function is achieved in our own society by the great organs of public opinion such as the journals, periodicals, and also by newspapers, newscasters and commentators.

The need for social appreciation is great in all human beings. All human beings are greatly dependent upon their fellows for their own well-being, making public opinion a most powerful means of control. To lose face in many societies is equivalent to losing what is most precious to one, one's reputation, and in several societies, such as in recent Japan, this calamity obliged the victim to take his own life.

Government

Government means the authoritative administration of public affairs. In all societies government is principally achieved through the agency of political forms and judicial and legal procedures.

Political Forms

Politics, although another name for government, is generally recognized as that part of governmental affairs which has to do with civil administration. The earliest form of government arises within the family, the principal authority being the head of the household. This is very nearly the form of government which prevails among the Australian aborigines, the Eskimos, and the Bushmen of South Africa. These peoples are characterized by being small in numbers, without chiefs, and living nomadic or seminomadic lives. They live at a subsistence level and lack any form of organized warfare. Nevertheless, each of these subsistence societies has a council of wise men. These are the men who have shown wisdom in their conduct, and no matter how young or old they may be, they are the persons who convene and act as the government of the group when matters of weight are to be decided. The band, a group of associated families, provides the first occasion for government of the group. The band tends to be a politically independent organization.

With settled life in villages or settlements, sedentary populations assume a more politically interdependent organization. The factor of settled residence seems to be of cardinal importance in the increase in the complexity of political life. As one of the accompaniments of increased political organization, "graft" appears quite as often as it does in the so-called highly civilized societies. Government serves as a means of channeling collective action and social control, and this justifies it to the governed. At the same time those in authority find themselves in a position to do well by themselves. Power seems to exert a corrupting effect upon many human beings. In most societies as long as the rulers serve the community adequately, preserve law and order, and do not exploit their position too violently, the people are content enough to accept them for what they are.

In North and South America, government among nonliterates was mostly democratic. A good example is the League of the Iroquois, the federation known as "The Five Nations." The tribes forming the League were the Mohawk, Oneida, Onondaga, Cayuga, and Seneca. Each tribe maintained its independence in its own affairs, but in matters affecting the League, a council of fifty, drawn unequally from each tribe, acted for all. Public opinion was always given the fullest scope for expression before the council, whose decisions were arrived at by majority vote. Women named the members of the council, though no woman served on it. Women could also remove any member of the council at will.

By means of governmental institutions, a number of communities may be organized into a larger organized group. If the *tribe* is the social entity distinguished by its community sentiment due to a common culture, the *state* may be regarded as the political entity characterized by common governmental organization. State organization has been characteristic of many nonliterate societies, but these societies are usually of an advanced type. The Iroquois League provides an example of a nonliterate state, and so do the numerous highly organized populations of West, North, and East Africa. The forms of political control which states exhibit are termed as follows:

1. Oligarchy—supreme power vested in the hands of a small exclusive class
2. Monarchy—supreme power vested in the person of a king
3. Gerontocracy—government by old men

4. Democracy—supreme power vested in the people and exercised by them directly or indirectly

5. Theocracy—government by supernatural direction, through priests or other sacred agents

It must suffice to say here that every one of these forms of government is to be found among existing nonliterate peoples.

Judicial and Legal Procedure—The Law

Law is one of the several means of control, and there has probably never been an enduring society without some system of law. *The* law represents the measures taken by those in authority to enforce conduct deemed essential to the stability of society. *A* law is a rule of conduct imposed by authority, the breaking of which rule renders the individual liable to punishment. The rules and the punishments are accepted by the community as binding. Enforcement of the law implies that the community sanctions the application of physical force, whenever necessary, in fulfilment of the law.

In the simpler food-gathering societies, the force of public opinion, or a decision arrived at by democratic procedure, may be implemented by the authorized physical force of the group or some punitive measure. The community or the council acts as the court.

As societies progress, customary legal practices become codified into full-fledged laws and legal systems. Even in the most advanced societies, the court will usually recognize a long-established custom as having the force of law. In nonliterate societies no rigid distinctions—if any are made at all—are made between custom and law. Law may develop as a social necessity, but it is a necessity which the individual recognizes in all societies. In all societies the individual obeys the law not because he considers it right to do so, but because it is in his self-interest to do so. When it is not in his self-interest to obey the law, he will either break it or attempt to evade it, and if there are a sufficient number of individuals who feel strongly enough about it, the law will be changed. Thus the force of public opinion is stronger than any law, for it is public opinion that makes the law.

Law, like every other social institution, is functionally related to the structure of the society of which it is a part. We would consider it a crime to abandon a baby or our old parents, but the Eskimos consider this a perfectly proper and even kind thing to do. Murder is not a matter for group action among the Eskimos; it is privately avenged. Nevertheless, in spite of the fact that there are no rulers or headmen among the Eskimos, the members of an Eskimo group will combine to get rid of one of their own people who has become a nuisance, as we have already seen, or they will rise up as a group against evil-doing sorcerers.

A *crime* is a wrong committed against the community or state, a *tort* is a private offense, such as a trespass or nuisance, and though they may not give them such names, nonliterate peoples make the distinction, more or less. Thus, the Eskimo regards the uncooperative member of the group as a criminal. The murderer's offense is a private one until he commits a second murder, when the offense becomes a matter for the group. The evil sorcerer is a criminal; the felonious assaulter is not.

Not all societies consider witchcraft a crime. A Crow Indian simply utilized his own countermagic or that of a friendly shaman. Many tribes punish incest with death or expulsion, but the Crow Indians, though disapproving of the act, did no more than deprecate it. In England suicide is regarded as a crime: self-murder. In the United States it is regarded as an occasion for sympathy. Civilized, as well as nonliterate, peoples differ among themselves as to what they regard as a crime.

Judicial Procedures

In the simplest societies the judges are the people. Where the family is the law, it is the father who is the judge. Where a council of elders can be called into being, they constitute the judges, and such peoples as the Australian aborigines will hold trials by council and hand down judgments of which any civilized court might be proud. Trial by jury is quite recent, its beginnings going back to the tenth century in France, but trial by court is found among many nonliterate peoples. The council of the Australian aborigines acts as a court, and so does the tribal council of an American Indian pueblo. The court, in all probability, is of very great antiquity, for wherever several duly empowered individuals get together to hear a case and deliver a judgment, we have a court.

Among the Yurok Indians of California an aggrieved Yurok would engage the services of two nonrelatives from another community, and the defendant would do the same. These legal representatives were called "crossers," because they crossed back and forth between plaintiff and defendant. The two parties involved, the litigants, never saw each other during this time. After hearing all the testimony from each side and pleading the relevant law, the crossers rendered a decision according to the rule in such cases. For their efforts these "lawyers" received a piece of shell currency called a "moccasin."

Regular court sittings are not held among most nonliterate peoples, but they are typical of many African societies. The sittings often afford opportunities for the exhibition of forensic eloquence and also frequently serve as general entertainment for the public. In the simpler African societies, the public attending the legal sessions may ask the litigants and the judges questions, but the judges decide upon and render the decision. In the more complex African societies such as the Ashanti (numbering over 200,000 members), judicial procedures are highly developed. Among the crimes that the Ashantis punish by death are murder, attempted suicide, certain sexual offenses, certain kinds of assault, certain kinds of stealing, cursing the chief, treason, cowardice, sorcery, violation of royal legislation, violation of a tabu, certain forms of abuse, and a woman calling a man a fool!

The king had the power of life and death, and no one might exercise that right but he. Private disputes could be settled between the household heads of the disputants. The tribal chief usually presides as high judge of his particular village or of the group of villages under his jurisdiction. As high judge he would be assisted by associate judges consisting of the elders of the group. But the supreme court justice is the king. Since the Ashanti kingdom is a constitutional monarchy, the king, as in most monarchies, has the power to pardon and to modify a sentence, which, for a consideration, he not infrequently does.

Among the Jagga of East Africa it is considered unseemly to bring a private issue before the court. Public opinion holds that proper decorum requires that the plaintiff summon the defendant to the public common, where the community, presided over by the headman of the village, listens to both sides and then delivers an umpire's judgment. Payment of fees is eliminated, though a gift to the headman and a beer feast to one's neighbors are customary. There is no physical enforcement of the decision. The tribal chief takes no part in the proceedings, but is usually informed of what has occurred. A regular trial before the chief's court is an elaborate affair, and verdicts are strictly enforced.

Everywhere the function of the law is to maintain order within society so that individuals may know what their rights, privileges, and duties are; this implies, of course, the recognition of the rights, privileges, and duties of others.

The functions of law, then, are: (1) the ordering of relationships between individuals, and between individuals and social groups, (2) the enforcement of the orders agreed upon by the community, (3) the just settlement of disputes between individuals and of offenses against the community, and (4) the adjustment of the rules of law to the changing conditions of life.

13

Religion

IN NONLITERATE SOCIETIES religion is the main bond which binds human beings together—the bond of relatedness. No people of whom we have knowledge is without a religion. The religious state everywhere takes the form of an emotionally felt relatedness to the forces and powers outside the orbit of embodied things, forces and powers which to a large extent control the fate of human beings and which human beings can to some extent control. The disembodied forces or powers are supernatural or spiritual, and a minimum definition of religion is the belief in the supernatural or as E. B. Tylor defined it (1871), "the belief in Spiritual Beings."

The Origin of Religion

Concerning the origin of religion, it is possible to speak only conjecturally. There have been many theories. Modern scholars derive the word itself from the Latin *religare,* "to bind to-

gether." Herbert Spencer (1820–1903), the English sociologist, thought that it arose out of ancestor worship. Sir James
Frazer (1854–1941) believed that it developed out of magic,
and others have thought it came into being as a result of the
interplay of such emotions as awe, fear, and wonder of the
supernatural (*pre-animism*). Still others have thought of religion as a normal psychological adjustment by which societies
build a protective barrier of fantasy against fear. Emile Durkheim (1858–1917), the French sociologist, regarded religion
as the most primitive of all social phenomena. It is out of religion, he wrote, "that there have come, by successive trans-
formations, all the other manifestations of collective activity,
law, morality, art, science, political forms, etc. In the beginning, all is religious." According to Durkheim the origin of
religious experience was to be sought in the collective elevation of feeling (euphoria) that occurred when individuals
came together in the larger gatherings of the tribe, which was
a reaction to the comparative flatness of secular life. Possibly
there is something of truth in all these theories.

The anthropologist surveying the great variety of patterns
of human experience, as he finds them at the present day, has
great difficulty in reconstructing the history of that experience.
One thing, however, is clear in the study of religious experience: the universe is presented to every people as something
of a mystery, a universe of mysterious but powerful forces.
In every known people we find the individual and the group
striving to relate themselves to these powerful forces. To this
elementary subjective experience, we usually give the names
"religious" or "spiritual."

In many areas of the Western world there are thousands
who put their religious energies into the worship of some
ideology. Soviet Russians are wedded to the belief in com-
munism, the communization of humanity. There is in this

system, of course, a full-panoplied pantheon of deities and other supernaturals, who are regarded with awe, reverence, fear, and wonder.

The Nature of Religion

The individual in society at once feels very close to and very far from other human beings, but always there remains the strongest of desires, to be related to one's fellow man. Human beings have devised no more successful means of achieving this relatedness than religion. When one combines the emotional experience of the world as a mystery with the craving to solve some part of that mystery by identification with the powers that be, and with the feeling of relatedness and loneliness, one understands something of the matrix out of which the religions of all peoples grow.

The Australian aborigines are a deeply religious people, and like some others, they have no gods. If you ask the Central Australian aborigines of the Arunta tribe, Who created the world? they will tell you that in the *alchera*—that is, in the far, far away "dream time" (meaning long before human memory)—there dwelt in the western sky two beings, who are described as *Numbakulla*—that is, self-existing beings who came out of nothing. *Numbakulla* are formless beings. They did not create the world—the Australian aborigines do not presume to know who did; it all happened so long ago, in the time of the dreaming, in the *alchera*. It happened one day that *Numbakulla* discerned, far away to the east, a number of *Inapertwa*, rudimentary human beings or incomplete ones, who possessed neither limbs nor senses, who did not eat, and who were all doubled into a rounded mass, in which just the vague outlines of the various parts of the body could be seen. These *Inapertwa*, who were destined to be transformed into men and women by the *Numbakulla,* represented the intermediate stage in the transformation of animals and plants into men. When the *Numbakulla* came down to earth and fashioned the *Inapertwa* into human beings, each individual

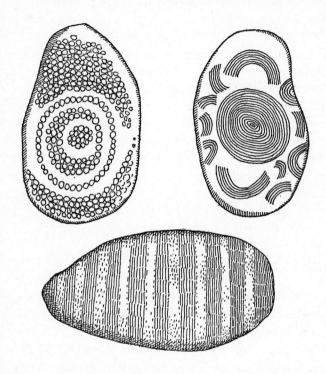

FIG. 33 *Australian painted totemic stones (churingas)*

naturally retained an intimate relationship with the animal, plant, or natural phenomenon of which he was indirectly a transformation, and with which he was at one time identical. It was in this way that human beings came into existence, and it is for this reason that each aboriginal possesses a *totem*, that is, an animal, plant, or natural phenomenon—such as water, wind, sun, fire, cloud—with which the individual is closely identified. It is to that plant, animal, or phenomenon that the aboriginal believes himself to owe his original creation.

Numbakulla no longer exist, but the aborigines still celebrate them in religious ritual, though they do not offer any sacrifices to them or worship these no longer existing beings. Even though the aborigines have no gods, they have a full-fledged religion in their cosmogony, in their belief in guardian spirits, in rite of prayer, and in their belief in the existence of the soul. The criterion of the sacred for the aboriginal is the totem, but it is not the totem as such that is sacred, but what might be called its principle or spiritual essence. It is this essence which renders the totem sacred. Durkheim claimed that totemism is the most primitive form of religion, yet we know of many peoples who exhibit no evidence of ever having passed through a totemic stage of development.

Spiritual Essence—Mana

The belief in a spiritual or totemic principle that we encounter in Australian aboriginal religious belief, we also encounter among many other nonliterate peoples. The belief in such a supernatural power was first described by Bishop R. H. Codrington in 1891 as occurring among the Pacific Melanesians. These people called that supernatural essence *mana*. Mana is a supernatural power or influence which is responsible for everything beyond the power of men, and it is something that works quite beyond the common processes of nature. "It is present in the atmosphere of life, attaches itself to persons and things, and is manifested by results which can only be ascribed to its operation. When one has got it he can use it and direct it, but its force," wrote Codrington, "may break forth at some new point; the presence of it is ascertained by proof." For example, a stone in the rough shape of some animal, tucked under one's belt, will bring success in the hunt, because of its wonderful power, the mana. A stone with the shape of a fruit, buried in the ground, will greatly increase the normal yield. Anyone and anything can have mana. There is no predicting what will and what won't have mana, but one thing is held to be certain: some things and some people, for some unknown reason, just don't have it. It's a matter of luck, but it certainly isn't luck itself. The idea of luck largely does not exist among most nonliterate peoples. The element of chance as it is understood among ourselves is largely unknown, for in nonliterate societies everything, as a rule, has a determinate cause. Mana is an attribute or quality of supernatural power of the thing itself, or becomes so by attaching itself to anything. And it works of itself; one doesn't have to manipulate it or enter into any relation of any kind with it. It is this difference which distinguishes it from *animism*, the belief in spirits with whom one has to enter into relation. Mana is powerful of itself; spirits are powerful only in certain relations.

Ideas similar to mana are found all over the world, though they may be called by very different names. Mana, it should be clear, does not imply the existence of supernatural beings but refers to an impersonal, wonderful power, which may be likened to a supernatural voltage with which the universe is imagined to be charged. Many nonliterate peoples do not make a clear distinction between this power as personal and the same power as impersonal. Among American Indian tribes, the terms *manitou* (Algonquian), *orenda* (Iroquois), and *wakanda* (Sioux), which are different names for a power similar to mana, may be either personal or impersonal and may mean either supernatural power in the abstract or a specific supernatural being. Sometimes these terms may be applied to a holy man or a religious practitioner. In one form or another, the idea of a wonderful supernatural power is found among most peoples. Furthermore, man's attempts to relate himself to this supernatural power, and the beliefs that grow out of them, lead to religious behavior.

The Techniques of Religion

In order to make the world intelligible to himself, man creates it anew in terms of his own experience; he brings the world, as it were, under domestication. The figures he projects into it are images compounded of the moral necessities which the authority figures of his experience, whether in the form of parents, teachers, rulers, or conscience, have urged upon him. As Ruth Benedict (1887–1948) has put it: "He sees in the external world the playing out of a human drama actuated by moral significance; that is, he sees it humanly directed toward rewarding those who have performed their required obligations and denying those who have failed in them. He is no longer in a blind and mechanistic universe. This wishful thinking, which is embodied in the religions of the world, and is worked out conceptually in mythology and theology and behavioristically in the religious techniques of petition and rapport, ranks with the great creations of the human mind."

Inherent in these religious techniques is the imperative urge of the believer to act—to act according to the requirements of his beliefs and according to the nature and meaning of the universe as revealed to him. The urge to act in this way constitutes the moral and social implications of all true religious experience, and gives rise to the religious techniques that are almost universally found in human groups: *magic,* the attempt to compel the supernatural; *reverence,* the combination of awe with love and admiration which one offers to the supernatural powers; *divination,* control by foreknowledge of supernatural power; *sacrifice,* control by gift, in which one puts the supernatural powers under compulsion to repay the gift by doing what one wants, or else simply desires to please the supernatural powers; *tabu,* control by abstention because one fears the supernatural powers; *fetishes* and *amulets,* two aspects of religious behavior—supernatural power treated as an attribute of objects makes amulets of those objects, and when the objects are treated as the seat or house of spirits, they constitute fetishes; *prayer,* the communication with the supernatural powers through speech. In addition, there is the belief in *guardian spirits,* widespread among the American Indians, where one may either place oneself in communion with a guardian spirit and at his service, or he places himself in communion with you and at your service.

Compulsion and rapport are the two extremes of religious behavior by means of which one enters into relation with the supernatural powers. In between these extremes there is every possible degree of compulsion and rapport and combinations of both. The techniques mentioned are the forms of behavior which are to be found in all the religious systems of which we have any knowledge.

Ceremonialism and Ritual

The forms which religions assume in different groups are as various as they could possibly be, and so is the pervasiveness of religion in any culture. Among the Polynesian Samoans supernaturalism is at a minimum, whereas it virtually occupies the whole life of the Polynesian Maoris of New Zealand. On the whole, nonliterate peoples are more pro-

foundly religious than civilized ones. Among the Zuñis of the
Southwest, religion is highly formalized, whereas the practices
among the Chukchee of Siberia are relatively informal. This
brings us to the matter of *ceremonialism*. Ceremonialism is
not inevitably rooted in religious faith, but it is a form of
behavior which is usually, though not always, associated with
religious acts. It may be defined as a body of formal, sanctioned observances, learned by observation or precept, that
indicate an attitude of reverence toward the supernatural.
Ceremonialism takes on the character of *ritual* when the order
of words or the pattern of behavior is thought to have inherent
virtue or power to produce results. In its secular form, ceremonialism becomes pageantry. Secular pageantry has, of
course, often been taken over for the purposes of religious ceremonialism. The function of both ceremonialism and ritual is
essentially to provide a collective or group participation in the
solemnization of collective behavior, to yield a collective sense
of the importance of that behavior.

Religion and Morality

While the religious systems of the Western world, indeed,
all the higher ethical religions, are concerned with the conflict between good and evil, many of the nonliterate religions
are more or less unconcerned with this aspect of life. In such
cultures the relatedness which the individual feels toward his
supernatural powers may, as far as his fellow men are concerned, be dealt with in secular terms. And ethical sanctions
may be largely a matter of secular concern, though religious
sanctions may often be massed behind them at many points.
Religion and morality are not, however, identified in such
cultures. At the present day, we are witnessing in the Western
world, at one and the same time, the emergence of a strong

secular conception of morality based on science and experience and a return to revealed religion and some of its more secularized counterparts, such as the various Reformed versions of Christianity.

The Meaning of Religion

Everywhere men have evolved religious systems in which religious behavior has repeatedly and independently been calculated to secure similar ends. This fact bears testimony to the unity of the human mind. Everywhere the religious experience creates the atmosphere and attitudes enabling human beings to regulate their conduct in the world in which they find themselves. With the development and deepening of the meaning of the religious experience within the matrix of an increasingly complex social world, human beings begin to understand that the communion with the supernatural powers must be extended to the communion with one's fellow human beings, and finally to a moral obligation of fellowship that is universal.

The anthropologist observes that the freedom to develop and subscribe to any religion one chooses in a democracy leads to the democratization of religion, and thus gradually to closer understanding among people, which unbending orthodoxies have before successfully prevented. In the religions of the world the anthropologist sees the unceasing struggle of humanity toward the attainment of the community of man, the reverence for life and the destiny of man which, in a mysterious universe, gradually lead the anthropologist to the discovery that the way of humanity must inevitably be through the path of cooperation.

14

Mythology and Philosophy

WHAT IS MAN? What is life? What is death? These are
questions that every people has asked, and attempted
to answer. When the question relates to the supernatural, to
the great questions of creation, the answers usually take the
form of a myth. A myth may be defined as a traditional story,
accepted as historical, embodying the beliefs of a people concerning the creation, gods, the universe, life, and death.
Legends and folk tales are often hard to distinguish from
myths. When stories account for the origins of things and are
believed to have taken place in a remote (mythical) past, they
are classed as myths. Legends may or may not be based on
historical events, and whatever they describe generally refers
to historic time. Folktales, or the folklore, of a people are a
people's unrecorded traditions as they appear in its customs,
beliefs, magic, and ritual.

The Function of Myth

The worldwide study of myths strongly indicates that man is a myth-making animal. His myths indicate the play of the imagination upon the raw materials of life, and the conversion of these, by a wishful-thinking imagination, into acceptable explanations and reassurances. In myth, the universe and everything in it is remodeled to the heart's desire. The myth-makers usually elect themselves as the chosen people or as the first and originally created people, and they recast the universe to function, as it were, in more humanly controllable terms. The discomforts of life, and the mysteries of the universe are, in myth, rendered understandable and even justifiable; hence, life is rendered more secure and tolerable than it would otherwise be.

Just as we sometimes tend to daydream, imagining ourselves in all sorts of pleasant situations, so the tendency of the human mind has been to institutionalize the "group daydreams." This tendency exhibits man, to some extent, in control of the universe by his habit of explaining it.

Mythology and folklore are not philosophic attempts to explain "the nature of things," though the desire to explain is usually there, but they are to be understood rather as arising out of man's desire to bring the universe into some sort of manageable form through the play of the imagination.

The Function and Dissemination of Folktales

The function of folktales is very similar to that of myths. In the folktale we are dealing with a novelistic activity among nonliterate peoples, which occurs, of course, without benefit of the written word. The free play of the imagination upon the everyday experiences of life is sufficient to account for the origin of folktales.

Folktales have been studied by experts the world over, and it has been found that many elements in tales, and also complete tales, have traveled over great distances and been incorporated into the culture of many different peoples. Some tales have even been traced to their origin, and then followed throughout the world. For example, in *Grimm's Fairy Tales* there is the famous story of "The Musicians of Bremen." This is the story of the despised and rejected animals who set out for Bremen where they propose to become State Musicians. They frighten a group of robbers out of their hut (the robbers symbolizing mankind), and in spite of the latter's attempt to regain possession, they live on in the hut happily ever after. This tale has been traced from its origin in Central Asia, through Europe, India and the Indies, China, Russia, and among the American Indians. Parts of the tale undergo change, but in essentials it is generally recognizable as the same one.

Every culture adapts its tales to its own peculiar needs, and the same is true of myths. Hence, the study of folklore is most helpful in tracing the movements and contacts of peoples who have no written or other records of such movements or contacts. Folklore is one of the means by which the anthropologist is able to trace the *diffusion* of cultural traits.

Myth, Folktales, and Culture

Since it is found that myths and folktales are constructed out of the materials of everyday life, it is obvious that these forms of artistic activity are extremely valuable in throwing light upon the dominant cultural interests of a people. An expert, by interpreting myths and folktales, can often give a fairly good account of a culture, in some of its aspects at least, without knowing anything of the source of the myths and folktales. That the Pueblo Indians, for example, place much emphasis upon space relations in their daily lives, is reflected in their mythology. The concern of the Australian aborigines with animal life is fully reflected in their mythology.

Philosophy

Nonliterate man casts the net of thought over the whole world. Mythology and religion may be closely related, but where one grows out of man's everyday life, the other grows out of his concern with the supernatural. And so it is with his view of the world, which will be compounded of secular, religious, mythological, magical, and experiential elements all rolled into one.

Most nonliterate peoples are extreme realists. They are bent on bringing the world under control, and many of their practices are devised to insure that reality will perform according to their bidding. In the conviction that the spirits are on his side, a man may then make all the necessary preparations for the success of an expedition. Coercing reality to do one's bidding by manipulating it in the prescribed manner is, for the nonliterate, a part of reality.

It is necessary to understand that nonliterate peoples identify themselves very much more closely with the world in which they live than do the literate peoples of the world. The more "literate" people become, the more they tend to become detached from the world in which they live.

What happens *is* reality to the nonliterate. If ceremonies calculated to increase the birth of animals and the yield of plants are followed by such increases, then the ceremonies are not only connected with them but are part of them; for without the ceremonies the increase of animals and plants would not have occurred—so the nonliterate reasons. It is not that the nonliterate is characterized by an illogical mind; his mind is perfectly logical, and he uses it very well indeed. An educated white man finding himself suddenly deposited in the Central Australian desert would be unlikely to last very long; yet the Australian aboriginal manages very well. The aborigines of all lands have made adjustments to their environments which indicate beyond any doubt that their intelligence is of high order. The trouble with the nonliterate is not that he isn't logical, but that he applies logic too often, many times on the basis of insufficient premises. He generally assumes that events which are associated together are causally connected. But this is a fallacy which the majority of civilized people commit most of the time, and it has been known to happen among trained scientists! Nonliterates tend to adhere too rigidly to the rule of association as causation, but most of the time it works, and by the pragmatic rule what works is taken to be true.

Nothing could be further from the truth than the idea that nonliterates are utterly credulous, superstition- and fear-ridden creatures, without any capacity or opportunity for independent and original thought. In addition to good horse sense, the nonliterate usually displays much practical sense based on an appreciation of the hard realities of life. Listen to this American Indian, an intensely religious individual, recounting the essence of the instruction current in his tribe: "Help yourself as you travel along the path of life. The earth has many narrow passages scattered over it. Some day you will be journeying on a road filled with obstacles. If then you possess the means for strengthening yourself, you will be able to pass through these passages safely. Indeed, if you act properly (i.e. circumspectly) in life, you will never be caught off guard." As Paul Radin, to whom this was told, remarks, nothing more practical than this could well be imagined.

Nonliterates are obliged to be practical; their very lives depend upon being so. In order to make such practicality acceptable to the younger members of the group it has been necessary to endow it with supernatural sanctions, and to surround it with myth and legend. There are good, sensible reasons for many of the nonliterate practices that more sophisticated peoples tend to regard as either stupid or barbaric. Such practices are generally neither stupid nor barbaric but serve some very definite purpose.

The individual in nonliterate society is generally a much more closely knit member of the group than his opposite number in civilized societies of the Western world. But, contrary to general belief, the nonliterate usually enjoys a considerable amount of freedom of personal expression. There are many ways in which the individual can so express himself and at the same time contribute to the welfare of the group. The form of self-expression with which we are concerned at the moment is the philosophical variety.

In every nonliterate society we find at least as many philosophers as we do in the civilized societies of the Western world. Everyone is, of course, to some extent a philosopher, but the general opinion that such persons are rare in nonliterate societies requires particular correction. Indeed, in many a nonliterate society there are one or more doubters, usually in the older age grades, who are rather skeptical about some of the traditionally accepted beliefs. In *Primitive Man As a Philosopher,* Paul Radin gives this commentary of an Amazulu tribesman of East Africa on Unkulunkulu, the supreme deity of the people:

"When black men say Unkulunkulu or Uthlana or the

Creator, they mean one and the same thing. But what they say has no point; it is altogether blunt. For there is not one among black men, not even the chiefs themselves, who can so interpret such accounts as those about Unkulunkulu as to bring about the truth, that others too may understand what the truth of the matter really is. But our knowledge does not urge us to search out the roots of it; we do not try to see them; if anyone thinks ever so little, he soon gives it up and passes on to what he sees with his eyes, and he does not understand the real state of what he sees. Such then is the real fact as regards what we know about Unkulunkulu, of which we speak. We say we know what we see with our eyes, but if there are any who see with their hearts they can at once make manifest our ignorance of that which we say we see with our eyes and understand too.

"As to our primitive condition and what was done by Unkulunkulu we cannot connect them with the course of life on which we entered when he ceased to be. The path of Unkulunkulu through our wandering has not, as it were, come down to us; it goes yonder whither we know not.

"But for my part I should say, if there be anyone who says he can understand the matters about Unkulunkulu, that he knows them just as we know him, to wit, that he gave us all things. But so far as we see, there is no connection between his gift and the things we now possess.

"I say then that there is not one amongst us who can say that he knows all about Unkulunkulu. For we say, 'Truly we know nothing but his name; but we no longer see his path which he made for us to walk in.' *All that remains is mere thought about the things we like.* It is difficult to separate ourselves from these things and we make him a liar. For that evil which we like of our own accord, we adhere to with the utmost tenacity. If anyone says, 'It is not proper for you to do that; if you do it you will disgrace yourself,' yet we do it saying, 'Since it was made by Unkulunkulu where is the evil of it?' "

Many other examples of acute criticism could be cited from nonliterate peoples but space forbids. It should, however, be added that in nonliterate societies professional critics as such do not exist. The professional critics come into being for the first time when life becomes easier and men can find opportunities which will enable them to live and to be critical.

The right to freedom of opinion is strongly maintained in nonliterate societies as a rule. As among ourselves, the opinions held must not be expressed in bad taste nor must they outrage the received canons of decorum. A man's thoughts are real events, and they must be respected, however strange they may appear. Thought is, to the nonliterate as much a part of reality as is anything else that is real. As long as the individual's reality does not interfere with anyone else, he has the right to express himself freely. A man's personality must not be affronted or unnecessarily curtailed.

Since thought gives expression to the reality of life beneath the surface, it is considered as important to permit its adequate functioning as it is to encourage it. The right to freedom of thought is extended also to children, and one of the most striking facts reported by anthropologists is the respect that is almost everywhere offered children as personalities in their own right in nonliterate societies. Radin recounts how on one occasion, among the Winnebago Indians, desiring to purchase a pair of child's moccasins, he approached the father of the child on the matter. He was told that the moccasins were, of course, the child's. Upon being pressed, the father agreed to consult the child, who was about five years old, as to whether he cared to part with them. "The whole transaction took place in a perfectly serious manner. There was not the slightest flippancy about it. The child refused and that ended the matter."

It is the same respect for children which, doubtless, causes the Winnebago to assert, "If you have a child, do not strike it. If you hit a child, you will merely put more naughtiness into it."

Most nonliterate people take the view that the individual is responsible for his own conduct. His parents can provide him with the idea and the model of what that conduct should be, but it is up to him to do something about it. A supreme obligation of parents, therefore, is held to be their responsibility as educators of their children in the ideals and requirements of a good member of the group. Such a good member must not only be a cooperative person, but the male must also be proficient in the ways of earning a living, in tracking, hunting, and other manlike activities, while the female must likewise be accomplished in keeping house, food-gathering, and other such feminine activities. Parents who tend to fall short of their duties are met with much public criticism, and public opinion is usually a force sufficient to cause them to mend their ways.

Strength of character, wisdom, and loyalty to one's group are the principal traits emphasized in nonliterate societies. And then there is the sense of proportion which seems to be so marked a characteristic of the nonliterate's world view— the proper order of things in relation to each other. One must learn the limits of the natural order, not only that one may control it, but that one may obey it.

There is one thing that it is somewhat difficult to control, and that is death; but one can obey it. One can also make attempts to control it, and most peoples, nonliterate and literate, have attempted to do so through the doctrine of immortality, the belief in a life after death. Immortality, with its promise of a usually happier afterlife, has served to ease the sojourn on earth of many a human being, but, on the whole, nonliterates have a very realistic view of death. The concept of immortality is obviously born of wishful thinking, for death is a very evident and unavoidable reality. The problem, therefore, is to find some means of rendering it acceptable, of perhaps denying its reality altogether.

The Aivilik Eskimos, for example, do not regard death as a hard, unbearable fact. It is like sleep; after a little time, the body reawakens. When the body ceases to breathe, they regard this as but an event in a never-ending cycle. Death, like birth, is only an event in time, and life is above time. They maintain, therefore, that they can run all risks, squander their possessions, as well as their lives, because they are immortal; for life extends beyond death, beyond the corruption of the body. Indeed, the most difficult thing for the Aiviliks to believe in is death, an episode on the road of the immortal life of man. One mustn't make too much of life on earth. An Aivilik death chant begins, "Say, tell me now, was life so nice on earth?" the answer being, of course, that it wasn't, and that life hereafter is likely to be much nicer in comparison.

It is often erroneously assumed that because nonliterates respond to the presence of death with great stoicism they are wanting in feeling. This is far from being the case. In the first place, the expression of emotion in the presence of death takes different forms in different cultures. In some, as among the Australian aborigines, it is permitted in the form of wailing and mourning ceremonies, but in others emotion is strongly discouraged in such forms, as among many American Indian tribes.

Deep emotion is no less present among the Indians than it is among the Australians; its expression is simply made to take another form. At one funeral ceremony, a Winnebago Indian rose and addressed the visitors as follows: "It is said that we should not weep aloud and you will, therefore, not hear any of us making any utterings of sorrow. And even although we weep silently we shall smile upon all those who look at us. We beg of you all, consequently, that should you find us happy in mood, not to think any the worse of it."

Elsdon Best relates that when an old Maori chief was suddenly stricken ill and his aged wife began to lament for him, he calmed her with the words, "Do not lament. It is well. We have trodden the path of life together in fair weather and beneath clouded skies. There is no cause for grief. I do but go forward to explore the path." Such thoughts are enshrined in innumerable beautiful chants and poems composed by every people in response to deeply felt emotion. The Maori of New Zealand cherish the thought just quoted in the following poem:

> *The tide of life glides swiftly past*
> *And mingles all in one great eddying foam.*
> *O heaven now sleeping! Rouse thee, rise to power;*
> *And thou, O earth, awake, exert thy might for me*
> *And open wide the door to my last home,*
> *Where calm and quiet rest awaits me in the sky.*

Hand in hand with the largely objective view of death that nonliterates take is the objectivity of their view of life—the tragic view of life, the sense that life is "not all beer and skittles," that tragedy is an accompaniment of the process of human living, and that man must reconcile himself to this fact. Different nonliterate peoples have adjusted themselves to this fact in varying ways, some attributing the tragedy in life to man's own transgressions, while others attribute it to the very nature of things. The adjustment is very generally a realistic and sensible one. Some individuals take the tragic

element in life a little harder than others, while some settle
for regarding life as tragic in part, but also in part comic—
a tragicomedy. Wisdom, then, lies in coming to terms with the
facts of life. Since it is inevitable that human beings will suf-
fer losses, deprivation, and injustice, that they will come into
conflict with some, at least, of their fellows, and even loved
ones, and with society, and that much suffering will ensue, it is
best to be prepared. Though suffering is inevitable, it cannot
usually be foreseen; one cannot control or alter it. It is from
this feeling of helplessness that the tragic sense of life arises.
But clouds have silver linings, as is so well brought out in the
following Papago Indian "Song to Pull Down the Clouds":

> *At the edge of the world*
> *It is growing light,*
> *Up rears the light.*
> *Just yonder the day dawns,*
> *Spreading over the night.*

Speculation for its own sake occurs among all nonliterate
peoples, though it is not being suggested that this is a habitual
practice with everyone in the group, any more than it is with
all the members of civilized populations. Radin gives this remarkable example, which must represent many others, of an
Oglala Indian's attempt to explain the significance of the
circle for his people:

"The Oglala believe the circle to be sacred because the great
spirit caused everything in nature to be round except stone.
Stone is the implement of destruction. The sun and the sky,
the earth and the moon, are round like a shield, though the
sky is deep like a bowl. Everything that breathes is round like
the body of a man. Everything that grows from the ground
is round like the stem of a plant. Since the great spirit has
caused everything to be round mankind should look upon the

circle as sacred, for it is the symbol of all things in nature except stone. It is also the symbol of the circle that marks the edge of the world and therefore of the four winds that travel there. Consequently it is also the symbol of the year. The day, the night, and the moon go in a circle above the sky. Therefore the circle is a symbol of these divisions of time and hence the symbol of all time.

"For these reasons the Oglala make their *tipis* circular, their camp-circle circular, and sit in a circle in all ceremonies. The circle is also the symbol of the *tipi* and of shelter. If one makes a circle for an ornament and it is not divided in any way, it should be understood as the symbol of the world and of time."

In this remarkable passage we perceive the functioning of the human mind at very nearly its highest level: the imaginative systematization of ideas, based upon what to others would be, for the most part, a series of bewildering experiences.

With respect to the systematization of ideas, nonliterate peoples have distinguished achievements to their credit. The Australian aborigines' creation beliefs constitute a complete evolutionary theory, foreshadowing the evolutionary theories which were later created by scientists. As we already learned, the aborigines postulated a time when there were no living things. These were then created by two formless spirits who later disappeared. There were at first no plants or animals, but only the precursors of these; then gradually these half-plants and half-animals, as they call them, were converted into real plants and animals, and from the latter men were eventually evolved. It is for these reasons that the aboriginal considers himself related to all natural things.

There are many similar stories of creation in different cultures. All of them represent man's attempt to explain the world to himself.

15

Science

WHAT IS SCIENCE? The Nobel Prize-winning physicist P. W. Bridgman has described it as doing one's utmost with one's mind. And that, of course, is what most scientists try to do. If that is what makes one a scientist, then many scientists have appeared among nonliterate peoples. But, of course, such a description of science is a bit too general, for doing one's utmost writing a story or making a better figure at ice-skating doesn't necessarily make those activities scientific. We must therefore settle for the usually accepted definition of science: *systematized knowledge* or *a system of facts and principles concerning any subject*. Science must be distinguished from the mere application of rules and methods, which is *technics*. Scientific procedures have usually been followed in arriving at those rules and methods, but it is the intellectual procedures that have been used and not the rules and methods themselves that constitute science.

A laboratory technician is not a scientist. He is a technician only. The person who has devised the methods the technician is using is the scientist. In this sense there are scientists as well as technicians in nonliterate cultures. In fact, in most nonliterate cultures everyone is a technician in one or more materials, but scientists are no more frequent than they are in any peasant society of the Western world.

Consider the following: Suppose people were born into a culture where no one knew how to make fire, where people had seen forest fires but were scared to death of them. How long do you think it would take to discover how to make fire and put it to use? The fact is that it might take a very long time, hundreds of thousands of years perhaps. When Professor A. R. Radcliffe-Brown studied the Andaman Islanders during 1906–08, he discovered that they knew of no way to make fire other than by kindling it from another ignited piece of wood. Fires were carefully kept alive in the village and carefully carried when traveling. The Andamanese showed great skill in carefully selecting wood that would smolder for a long time without going out and without breaking into a flame.

In order to put fire to use, one must first *predict* a use for it. One must see ahead clearly what it will be able to do; in other words, a theory must be developed to the effect that if one could capture and control fire one might be able to make it do one's bidding. Thinking of this kind is the essence of science. For example, as far back as the fourth century B.C. Democritus (460?–370? B.C.) suggested that matter was made up of tiny particles, imperceptible to the senses, which he called atoms. This was a theory. It took over two thousand years to prove that theory correct by the demonstration of the actual existence of the atom. The man who first thought of capturing fire for human use was every bit as great a genius as was Democritus. He is one among the thousands of unsung benefactors of the human race. Prometheus is the name the ancient Greeks gave to the Titan who first taught man the use of fire. The word "Prometheus" means "forethought," and forethought is the father of invention. The tale is that he made man of clay, and, in order to endow the clay with life, stole fire from heaven and brought it to earth in a hollow tube. Similar stories come from numerous cultures other than the Greek.

Having, then, with forethought foreseen the value of controlled fire, the next step was to capture it. How this was achieved we do not know. There are many theories but none can be proven. One theory suggests itself with great force, and this is based on the coincident appearance of flint-chipping and fire. The suggestion is that in chipping his flints, prehistoric man could not have failed to observe the similarity of the sparks to the fire induced from natural causes—lightning-struck trees, prairie and forest fires, perhaps the rubbing of dry twigs against each other in a high wind, or maybe fires induced by volcanic action. It may be that fire was independently discovered by different groups of men in different ways. We don't know. But what we do know is that someone did test the theory that if one reproduced the conditions under which fire was naturally caused, the probability was that one could produce it artificially. This was a piece of scientific reasoning and experiment, and it succeeded. Methods of making fire vary in different nonliterate groups. The earliest known use of fire by man is associated with Peking man (*Sinanthropus pekinensis*), but how he made his fire, or whether he simply used it as the Andamanese do, we do not know.

Methods of Making Fire

Since the variety of methods of making fire illustrate the scientific uses of the imagination, they may briefly be described here. Small nodules of iron sulfide (iron pyrites) are of common occurrence. When two pieces are accidentally knocked together, they give off sparks. The forcible striking or two sulfides, or one sulfide and a piece of flint, chert, quartz, chalcedony, or other siliceous stone, is the method of *percussion*. The evidence points to the fact that in the Old Stone Age, fire was made by the use of flint and pyrites—a method still in use among the Eskimos, the Fuegians, and some American Indian tribes. Tinder in the form of dried moss or fungus, the down of floss or seeds, and dry and rotten wood seems to have been discovered early and widely used. Astonishing as it may seem to those of us who are unacquainted with the fact, sparks can be struck from the most unpromising of materials. For example, in Southeast Asia— the Malay Peninsula and the Philippines—a rough-surfaced bamboo is struck with a piece of porcelain to produce sparks.

Fire by Wood-Friction

By the friction of one piece of wood upon another, wood-dust is produced. During the friction so much heat is generated that the little heap of wood-dust begins to smolder, and in a few seconds can be blown into a glowing flame. Fire may thus be produced in a few minutes or less. There are three principal primitive tools used for making fire by wood-friction: (1) the saw, (2) the plow, and (3) the drill. The wood that is held at rest on the ground is called the *hearth*. One either saws across the grain of the hearth, plows along it, or drills into it at right angles. The last method is the most widely distributed.

The Fire-Piston

The fire-piston is a very simple instrument which must have taken, however, the acutest observation and intelligence to devise. Its fire-making power depends upon the fact that if air in a confined space is abruptly compressed, heat is developed, which may then set fire to tinder. It is widely distributed through southeastern Asia. It consists of a narrow cylinder four to six inches long of bamboo, wood, or horn, and sometimes metal, closed at one end. Fitted tightly into

FIG. 34 *Fire-piston from southeast Asia*

the cylinder is a piston of similar material. At the lower end of the piston is a small depression in which the tinder is lodged. The piston, drawn to the top of the cylinder, is given a smart push to the bottom of the chamber, and on withdrawal the tinder is found to be alight. The instrument seems to have been first invented in Asia, and was not reinvented in Europe until the beginning of the nineteenth century, where it went out of use in 1827 with the introduction of the friction match.

The discovery of the fire-piston was almost certainly due to an accident of favorable observation by an acute intelligence. It probably did not involve the working out of the principle first and its application afterward. Nevertheless, the original discoverer was making quite as significant a scientific finding as was Sir Alexander Fleming when he observed in 1928 the effects of the penicillin mold upon his plate of bacteria.

One must make a sharp distinction between discovery by finding—a uranium deposit, a new star, or an Indian burial ground—and discovery by finding out. The latter involves the uncovering of the ways in which things work, their properties, and the conditions which relate events to each other, and finally it involves applying this knowledge to the accomplishment of a purpose. Observation, discovery, and application are the three processes involved. There can be no doubt that early man and nonliterate man of later times, to the extent that they indulged in scientific activities, did so in an intensely practical way and for exclusively practical purposes.

Agriculture was a scientific discovery of great practical value arising out of practical needs. The invention of many of the implements devised to assist the agricultural process, and many of the techniques used in planting, involved scientific thought. Practical or applied science is an accomplishment of every nonliterate people. It differs from that of more sophisticated societies in that it is generally applied on a smaller scale and to the solution of a comparatively limited number of problems.

Time-Reckoning

Of practical importance to some nonliterate peoples is a method of reckoning time in order that the coming and the going of the seasons may be predicted, the waxing and wan-

ing of the moon, the migration of animals, the rise and fall
of rivers, and so on. Every nonliterate people has some method
of reckoning time, though among some the method is much
more crude than among others. The simplest way to reckon
time is to note the relation between the appearance of one
event and another which follows it more or less regularly.
When certain plants blossom, for example, certain kinds of
animals also begin to make their appearance and others will
follow. The seasons are everywhere recognized, made use of,
and subdivided.

The Greenland Eskimos divide their seasons in correspond-
ence with the wanderings of animals, the position of the sun,
moon, stars, and other observations based on the regularities
of their environment. Most nonliterate peoples have a calendar, however crude in some cases, which is based on astronomical observations. It should be remembered that most nonliterates sleep out in the open, and during the night they are
able to make a far closer acquaintance with the stars in the
heavens than most civilized men ever do. There are few, if
any, nonliterate peoples who do not have names for the larger
stars and star clusters. The temporary appearance and disappearance of the stars is not a matter of random or occasional
observation with nonliterate peoples. They are therefore easily
able to associate other changing natural events, such as the
changing seasons, with the stellar changes, and thus use the
stars, the sun, and the moon to predict coming events. At the
same time they are able to count the time between the intervals.

The position of the sun, and the type of shadow it casts
upon any object, at particular times, in association with certain
natural events, drew the attention of many different nonliterate peoples. They observed that the sun is in the north
during one season and in the south during another (the two
solstices), and that the shadows cast upon the same object

in the same place vary not only with the hour but during different days of different seasons. The Australian aborigines have made excellent use of this observation.

The Australian aboriginal has a good idea of time. In referring to a past or future event, he will describe it by pointing to the assumed altitude of the sun. To fix a time for a proposed action, a stone is placed upon a cliff or in the fork of a tree, a day or two in advance, so that the sun strikes it exactly at the hour decided upon. When this occurs on the day of the proposed action, those involved know that it is the time agreed upon. Days are reckoned by the number of sleeps, and larger stretches of time are counted by the number of moons.

The Zuñi Indians of the American Southwest determine the beginning of their new year, and the time for planting and harvesting, by using a large, upright block of sandstone as a datum point for taking observations of the sun.

Volumes could be filled on the astronomical observations and the measurement of time among nonliterates. The examples cited here do serve to illustrate the fact that nonliterate peoples do, scientifically, attempt to measure the passage of time in order to bring the world under better control. We cannot, however, complete this section without some reference to those remarkable Vikings of the Sunrise, the Polynesians, who read the heavens and the tides so well that they were able to draw up the most elaborate and detailed guides to navigation. These navigation charts were remarkably accurate and helpful, and made the Polynesians the greatest navigators of their time—up to and even after Columbus.

Numbers and Measurement

The idea of number probably occurred very early in the history of man. The food-gathering peoples seem to have the least need for numbers in their daily lives, and therefore a study of the nonliterate food-gatherers probably shows something of the state of mathematical knowledge of early man.

The Australian aborigines vary in their methods of numeration. In general they have no running series of numerals. The Arunta of central Australia occasionally counted up to five, sometimes using their fingers in doing so, but frequently anything beyond four was indicated by the word *oknirra*, meaning much or great. One is *ninta*, two *terama* or *tera*, three *tera-ma-ninta*, four *tera-ma-tera*, five *tera-ma-tera-ninta*. There are words for "small number," "larger number," and "very large number." Slightly, but only slightly, more elaborate systems of counting than this are found among some tribes, such as the Dieri tribe near Lake Eyre in south-central Australia, who count in the same way as the Arunta, but up to eleven, bringing in the feet and toenails as well as the hands. The fact is that food-gathering peoples seem to have very little use for complex systems of numeration and therefore haven't developed any. It is when populations become large and the culture more complex that the mathematical processes are developed to meet the needs.

The Maya of Yucatan not only invented methods of addition and subtraction, but they also invented a symbol for zero and gave a value to their numbers according to zero's position. The Aztecs indicated 1 by a finger, 20 by a flag, 400 by hair, 8000 by a pouch.

Beam scales were invented by the Peruvians together with an original method of determining equilibrium.

In nonliterate societies there is little need for precise forms of linear measurement. Where, as among the Kwakiutl of Vancouver Island, measurement becomes essential in laying out the lines for a square house, considerable precision has been developed in the application of geometric principles. This is seen also in their manner of making boxes.

Such a thing as the objective standardization of measurements is rarely found among nonliterates, though a quasi-objectivity in linear measurements is reached in the widespread use that has been made of the proportions of man's own limbs. The length of the forearm from elbow point to tip of middle finger is a good primary unit for laying off lengths. The distance from outstretched thumb tip to outstretched little finger,

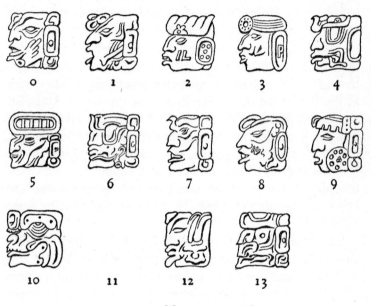

FIG. 35   *Mayan numerals*

roughly equal to half the forearm length, and the length from outstretched forefinger tip to little finger tip (the little span), equal to one third of the forearm, were obvious linear measures which suggested themselves. Others were the foot length, palm length, hand width (a horse still stands so many "hands" in height), and finger width (still a measure in modern medicine), and then, of course, there was the height of a man. The forearm length became the cubit, and four cubits made a fathom.

The use of notched sticks for making more or less exact measurements are in quite wide use among nonliterates, and cloth and other materials are often measured out by their use. Such sticks were also used in building boats by the Penobscot Indians of Maine.

For the measurement of volume, all sorts of familiar containers are used, from shells to baskets and canoes. Let it be recalled that the oilmen still measure the yield of their wells and the content of their reservoirs by the barrel, a reminder of the fact that oil, by sheer accident, happened to be transported first in barrels.

The techniques of smelting, extracting, and alloying ores involved many a scientific process, but these techniques were not really developed until about 3500 B.C. in the Near East. Copper, gold, and meteoric iron are surface ores found in relatively pure form, so that they require no smelting to make them usable. The Neolithic Badarians of Egypt were able to cold-hammer such ores into tools and ornaments, and several American Indian tribes that lived where surface outcroppings of copper were available did likewise. The Eskimos use bits of meteoric iron to make tools. Using these metals, the Aztecs and the Incas excelled in their fine work.

Ironworking is widespread, as is the smelting of iron ore, among African peoples, who may well have discovered the processes involved in forging, extracting, smelting, and manufacturing implements of all sorts. It is, however, believed by some authorities that the ironworking of the Africans, like that of the Europeans and Asiatics, diffused to them from the Near East. The oldest African datable iron tools are from Meroë in Nubia (700 B.C.).

Enough has been said to indicate that nonliterate peoples

are capable, under the pressing conditions of necessity, of doing their utmost with their minds to solve some practical problem in a scientific manner. Most of the scientific processes involved are of a practical nature, and there is little time or inclination for science for science's sake. The latter activity does not appear until the development of highly sophisticated societies like Hellenic Greece. This is but yesterday in the history of human time. Because the Greeks were an aristocratic society based on slavery, they, who had so much of the necessary theoretical knowledge at their disposal, virtually failed to apply it. Machines were unnecessary since slaves could do all the work. The Greeks were interested in ideas—in brains—not in drains. The refuse of civilization could be disposed of by slaves, but only those with the necessary leisure could create and maintain that civilization. The Greeks developed the greatest ideas in the humanities and the sciences that the world has ever known, and probably the fewest inventions of a mechanical kind. Not that the Greeks were uninterested in the practical application of some of their ideas, it is simply that they were not enamored of the possibility of creating machines that think and human beings who don't. With that, they clasp hands with the long millennia of nonliterate men.

16

The Arts

THOSE PURSUITS in which the imagination is chiefly engaged, in giving form and meaning to the materials with
which one works, are known as arts. In this sense the arts are
probably very old. There is no known people that is without
them—drawing, painting, carving, sculpture, music, poetry,
storytelling, and the dance.

To draw seems to be a natural potentiality which children
seek to express at the earliest possible opportunity. Without
any instruction whatever, small children will spontaneously
make drawings with the materials placed in their hands. Apparently apes will too, at least the gorilla will, for a young
gorilla has actually been observed tracing his own shadow with
his forefinger. This is not unrelated to the way children draw.
One little girl when asked what she did when she drew replied,
"First I think, and then I draw a line around my think."

Drawing in all its forms constitutes one of the languages of the imagination. Since it is the oldest form of art of which we have any record, perhaps we had better begin with it.

Drawing and Painting

Seventy-five years ago if anyone had suggested that prehistoric men were at least as intelligent as their modern descendants, he would have been greeted with derision. If he had gone on to suggest that there have been artists who lived more than ten thousand years ago whose artistic accomplishments could not be bettered by any artist who has lived since, his sanity might well have been questioned. And yet these statements are perfectly true, for the oldest known paintings by man do go back well over ten thousand years, and they display a really breathtaking skill and beauty.

The first discovery of prehistoric painting was made in 1879 near the village of Santillana del Mar about twenty miles west of Santander, Spain. Here, on the ceiling of a large cave that was named Altamira, paintings and drawings were discovered of such astonishing competence that for almost thirty years the experts refused to accept them as the work of prehistoric man. Many more caves had to be discovered showing the same kind of drawings and polychromes before the experts were at last forced to yield to the facts.

Often these drawings and paintings are found in the farthest recesses and darkest and most uncomfortable corners of the cave, and often, too, they show one drawing or painting superimposed upon another. The animals shown are mainly of extinct species in the southwestern European region—bison, wild boar, wild horse, mammoth, reindeer, ibex, antelope, woolly rhinoceros, cave lion, moose, musk ox, and several others. From the fact that these animals are depicted and that their fossil remains occur in the caves, together with the hearths of

the human inhabitants, it has been calculated, by radiocarbon
dating, that the cave paintinges made at Lascaux in central
France (discovered in 1940) were executed about fifteen thousand years ago. This happens to be almost exactly the estimate
that archaeologists had arrived at by other means.

It is interesting to follow the distribution of this cave art
from the Dordogne of central France southwest to Spain, for
it suggests a group of populations who were in touch with one
another, who clearly exhibit a number of cultural traits in common, of which their art was but one.

Why did these people of Aurignacian culture make the wall
paintings in uninhabitable caves, and in the darkest and most
inaccessible recesses of these? The most likely answer is that
they made them for magical purposes and not in order to
decorate the caves. The animals shown on the roofs and walls
of these caves are often represented as pierced by spears and
arrows. One makes as naturalistic a model as one can of the
animal one hopes to kill, and then kills it in effigy; as one does
to the drawing of the animal—accompanied by the proper incantations—so one will do in fact to the real animal. One has
but to wish in the ritually acceptable manner and one will
succeed. Hunting scenes abound in these cave drawings and
paintings, and there can be very little doubt that this art, at
any rate, was devoted principally to the practical purpose of
securing success in the hunt. This does not mean that the artist
did not obtain some esthetic pleasure from his achievement,
but it does mean that love of beauty was not the principal
purpose.

That the artist took pride in his accomplishment and was
encouraged to do so is indicated by several facts. In the first
place, the skill exhibited by these artists takes a certain amount
of training. That such training was available from different
centers is testified to by the fact that preliminary sketches on

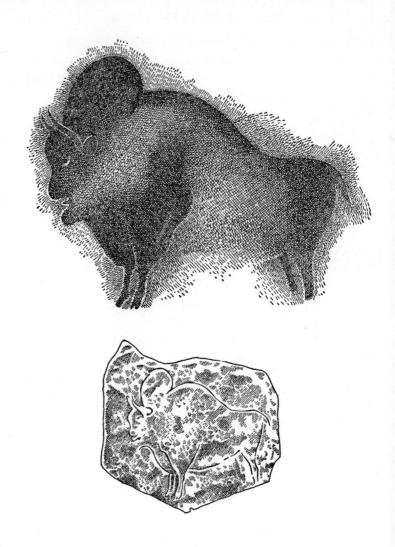

FIG. 36 *Presumed sketch-sheet and final cave painting*

stone of certain animals have been found several hundred miles away from the caves in which the finished polychromes occur. in 1926 an engraving on limestone was found in the half-cave at Genière in France. This was immediately recognized to be the sketch for the very individually painted polychrome of an old bison on the wall of the cave at Font-de-Gaume, in the Dordogne, some two hundred miles away.

Obviously artists who could paint as well as Aurignacian

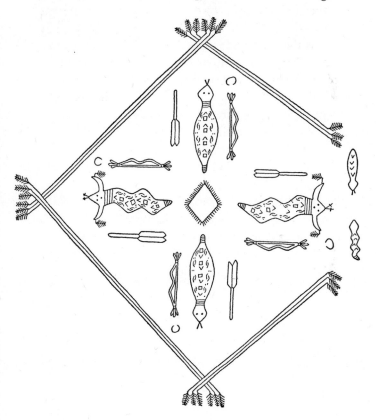

FIG. 37   *Navaho sand painting*

and Magdalenian cave artists must have taken great esthetic pleasure in accomplishing their work, whether inside or outside a cave. It is therefore unnecessary, as some have done, to argue that the first drawings and paintings were made only for magical purposes, only for a practical purpose, and not from the sheer pleasure derived from doing something for its own sake—and doing it as well as possible.

Some cave art persists among the Australian aborigines, which they indulge in for much the same magical purposes to this day as their Old Stone Age European relatives.

Perhaps the most undeveloped artists of the human species are the Indians of Tierra del Fuego who, apart from decoration of the body, and a few domestic objects with simple dot designs, do not display any further interest in art. All other nonliterate peoples exhibit a simply amazing variety of art forms which encyclopedias would be insufficient to describe, from simple decoration to the most complex religious productions, such as the beautiful sand paintings of the Navaho Indians.

Whether it be practical, magical, religious, decorative, the function which art serves in nonliterate cultures, if it can be said to have a single function, is to relate the individual to the group. Whatever is represented is calculated to interest and bring the group closer together in some way.

Literature

The unwritten literature, poetry and prose, of nonliterate peoples is often very highly developed. This literature is known to us only in translation, but those who are familiar with the native rhythms, if not with the languages, tell us that they are quite as beautiful as those which we find in the languages of the Western world.

The food-gathering peoples have a literature which matches

that of any more advanced people. Every tribe seems to have its poets and storytellers and their gifts are much appreciated among the nonliterate. In reading the recorded literature of nonliterates, it should always be remembered that it is in translation and that its native character has probably been profoundly changed by the Europeanization of the rhythms and even the meanings. The excellence of the original can therefore rarely be appreciated. The best work of its kind which preserves something of the spirit of the original as nearly as possible is Frank Hamilton Cushing's *Zuñi Folk Tales* (1901), and Verrier Elwin has done the same for the native peoples of Chhattisgarh, in the Central Provinces of India, in his *Folk-Songs of Chhattisgarh* (1946).

The theme of literature everywhere is life and death and all that happens in between. Every literature is in harmony with its cultural framework. Among nonliterates both poetry and prose are closely associated with song, most of the poems and even stories being either sung or accompanied by song. Rhythm in poetry and prose, as well as repetition, which is a form of rhythm, is markedly emphasized, and it is no accident that poetry, prosody, song, instrumental music, and the dance are all closely associated. The poetry and prose of the Old and New Testaments retain the devices of rhythm and repetition to a marked degree, traits which are characteristic of Near Eastern literature as a whole, and which are undoubtedly among the most ancient of all literary traits. Sometimes the repetition may be extended to great length, and sometimes, as in the following quatrain, used with great and ingenious skill. The poem is a Nootka Indian one and is entitled "Plaint Against the Fog":

> *Don't you ever,*
> *You up in the sky,*
> *Don't you ever get tired*
> *Of having the clouds between you and us?*

As among most nonliterates, the Copper Eskimos highly value those who are able to create new songs as well as dances, and almost everyone possesses this talent among the Copper Eskimos. Here is a Dance Song:

I am quite unable
To capture seals as they do, I am quite unable.
Animals with blubber since I do not know how to capture,
To capture seals as they do I am quite unable.
I am quite unable,
A fine kayak such as they have I am quite unable to obtain.
Animals that have fawns since I cannot obtain them,
A fine kayak such as they have I am unable to obtain.
I am quite unable
To capture fish as they do, I am quite unable.
To capture fish as they do, I am quite unable.
Small fish since I cannot capture them,
To capture fish as they do I am quite unable.
I am quite unable
To dance as they do, I am quite unable.
Dance songs since I do not know them at all,
To dance as they do I am quite unable.
I am quite unable to be swift-footed as they are,
I am quite unable . . .

Among the Copper Eskimos the dance song takes the place of the daily newspaper, for in the great Copper House where the Eskimos daily assemble, every important incident is recorded in dance song. Song and dance, poem and story serve not only to assist in binding the group together, in keeping it informed and alive by serving as the vehicles for traditional lore, for myth, ballad, and magic formula, but also serve as a means for reducing personal and interpersonal tensions. For these purposes many peoples provide opportunities for dramatic experiences, ceremonies, and plays, in which every member may play a part. That such experiences can have a beneficial effect was discovered by nonliterate peoples long before the development of modern psychology.

Music

All peoples sing, but many nonliterate peoples do not have any musical instruments except those used for expressing rhythm. When this is true, tone is provided by the human voice. Sometimes the range of melodies is limited to a few notes, and sometimes it extends over more than an octave.

While we divide the octave into twelve equal intervals, the Siamese divide theirs into seven, and the Javanese theirs into five equidistant steps.

The Australian aborigines sometimes use a tubular conch shell as a trumpet, but merely to enlarge the sound of the human voice. Reeds are also commonly used, and sticks, both to produce rhythm rather than tonality. The Bushmen and Hottentots use the musical bow and a reed pipe, and they sometimes fashion crude flutes. The elder men teach the young boys to play these instruments, and girls look with much favor upon the boys who excel. Drums and all sorts of other percussion instruments are widely used among nonliterate peoples. Gongs and the xylophone are used for melodic purposes, the former in southern Asia, the latter in Africa. Notched bones or sticks pulled over hollow vessels yield a rasping sound, and this has been used by many peoples. There are all sorts of original instruments, never used by us, which were invented by nonliterates. One is made of a block of wood which has been divided by deep curved notches into a number of sections. By striking the sections, or rubbing over them, different tones may be produced. This instrument comes from New Ireland in Melanesia. The African zanza consists of iron strips of different lengths stretched over a resonating box provided with a bridge. The strips are pulled at their ends like strings. String instruments seem to have been quite unknown in the Americas before the advent of the white man. In Africa they are widespread, the harp and the lyre being among the most frequent in the African world. The banjo is an African instrument.

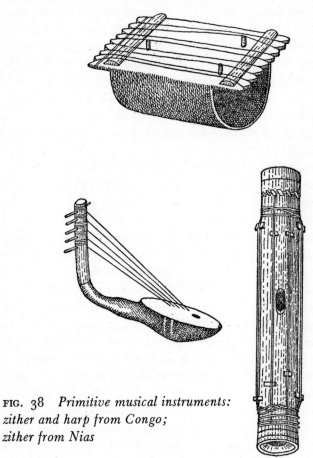

FIG. 38 *Primitive musical instruments: zither and harp from Congo; zither from Nias*

The Dance

The dance is almost certainly as ancient as song. Singing appears to be spontaneously accompanied by rhythmical movements of the body. Many of the cave drawings and paintings show unmistakable representations of various dances—women dancing around a man, a medicine man dancing, and the group as a whole dancing. Then there are various small groups dancing together. All these varieties of the dance occur among nonliterate peoples today, and they occur also among the more advanced societies. What is rare among nonliterate societies are joint dances where single couples stay together throughout the dance as among ourselves. Nonliterates dance all together; we tend to dance in pairs, with each couple dancing alone, not with the other couples. Furthermore, in the dancing of nonliterate peoples continuous body contact between the sexes is extremely rare.

As is true in almost everything else, the dance among nonliterate peoples is a group phenomenon, in which everyone actually or vicariously indulges. Occasionally a particular dance may be the property of a particular person. In New Ireland anyone who becomes enamored of a dance may, if the owner is willing, purchase it. In Africa even a particular step may be the property of some organization.

Dances may be indulged in for the purposes of amusement, or for ceremonial, religious, or esthetic purposes. Whatever the purpose, every culture has its own dances, and they are often of the greatest beauty, and even the least beautiful is likely to be interesting. The universal need for expression in rhythmical bodily movements is differently satisfied in different cultures, according to the stylized ways in each. But everywhere in nonliterate cultures the function of the dance is the same: to give expression to a need and to bind the dancer closer to his group. There is dancing for the sheer joy of it also, but even the form of this kind of dancing is largely determined by the group.

17

The Anthropologist in the Field

T HE OBSERVATIONS described in the preceding pages are
largely those made by anthropologists working in the field.
These observations represent, for the most part, a minute fraction of the work of many investigators who have been at work
during the last half century. One of the first lessons to be
learned from a short book such as this, which attempts to deal
with so large a subject, is that, far from having come to the
end of a book, one has, in reality, only come to the beginning
of many others. The Bibliography, which follows this chapter,
lists a number of books, briefly annotated, which are calculated to introduce the reader to the larger literature relating
to the various aspects of anthropology.

In the first chapter of this book, the reader was briefly introduced to anthropology. In this final chapter, I should like
to bring the reader up to date on what anthropologists are
actually doing at the present time.

Nonliterate cultures are disappearing or changing at so rapid a rate that there is literally not a minute to be lost in studying them. Cultures that have remained untouched by white civilization still exist, but as time goes on they will become fewer and fewer. Anthropologists have long realized this and have done all they could to have such cultures studied. Usually the anthropologist will have studied one or more nonliterate cultures in the field, and in training his students will require of them that they apply the theories and the techniques they have learned to the study and monographing of at least one nonliterate culture. The importance of such work cannot be overestimated. In the first place, insofar as the anthropologist himself is concerned, fieldwork is a necessary part of his training. Just as the internship is considered a necessary part of the training of a physician, so today internship in the field is considered a necessary part of the training of every anthropologist. The anthropologist who has not had the advantage of such field experience may achieve high competence as a theoretician in the particular aspects of anthropology that he has made his own and as a practical anthropologist may be indistinguishable from the best, but he will usually be lacking in a certain "feel" for, and a certain insight into, the nature and meaning of the cultures that have been studied by other anthropologists. There are, of course, exceptions to every rule, but there can be no question of the value of having undergone the experience of living with a people whose way of life differs so substantially from that in which any anthropologist is likely to have been brought up. Learning to see another people's way of life, its culture, objectively is in itself an invaluable experience. This is not only what the anthropologist tries to do himself, but also what he tries to teach other people to do.

In studying the manner in which the other half of the world conducts its affairs, we not only learn how remarkably various man's adaptations and adjustments to his environment can be, but we also learn much about the malleability of human nature. Not only that, we learn a great deal about human nature itself. Indeed, it is anthropology, and not psychology, which has been able to show how unsound is the old saying, "You can't change human nature." On the contrary, anthropology has illuminatingly and convincingly shown how changeable human nature is. The usual concomitant of the view that one cannot change human nature is that if one is to embark upon any form of social change without creating havoc, it must be done very gradually and over a long period of time. Recent studies—such as those of Margaret Mead in the Admiralty Islands, where the Manus have made the passage from the Stone Age into the Jet Air Age within a few years, with anything but catastrophic effects—indicate that the rate of social change can proceed at quite an accelerated pace under reasonably favorable conditions. In the United States one often hears it said that in connection with the changing status of the Negro it is necessary to "go slow." This is often a rationalization for not going at all, for it may well be asked, How slow? Nevertheless, there can be no denying the fact that in some regions of the United States the conditions are such that a longer-range kind of planning is indicated. Even so, with the fact of desegregation before us, we have a field experiment in our very midst which we can observe and study. There were those who said that it would take many generations before desegregation could ever be accomplished in the United States. The evidence before us is that such judgments were essentially unsound. In spite of certain expected reactions in some parts of the country, desegregation has gone through quite smoothly and in a vastly shorter period of time than even many an expert thought possible. Desegregation, now an accomplished fact in the majority of communities, represents a social change of major significance that has been brought about with almost complete success in less than a year of time.

In a world in which there exist many nonliterate peoples, and many quasi-literate peoples, who are destined increasingly to feel the influence of the technologically developed peoples of the world, it is helpful to understand that the social changes which such peoples are able to undergo without injury to themselves can proceed at quite a rapid rate.

It is also important to understand that great care and study of the conditions are necessary before such programs of change are undertaken. Frederick the Great had to persuade his peasants to eat potatoes by sending uniformed gendarmes among them. Count Rumford (1753–1814), head of the ordnance and army of the elector of Bavaria, had to force soldiers to cultivate and consume potatoes so that they acquired the habit and took it with them among their people after they left the army. In the matter of food, people are particularly apt to be conservative, for the most irrational reasons, as case report after case report from the field has in recent times shown us. After going to the greatest trouble to persuade the Spanish-American farmers living in the Rio Grande Valley of New Mexico to substitute the growing of hybrid corn for their own poor variety, the whole scheme foundered, much to the distress of the United States Department of Agriculture, on the simple fact that the women didn't like the new corn. The men found it easier in every way to grow, the crop gave three times the yield of the native corn, the quality was superior, but all the wives had complained from the first. Its texture was wrong; it didn't hang well together for tortillas; the tortillas came out the wrong color; and so on. So the inferior native corn was replanted and the superior hybrid corn abandoned. Domestic harmony was restored; tortillas looked and tasted as they always had, and once again custom declared itself king.

The moral of this story is that when one is proposing to help a people improve its lot by changing its habits, it is first necessary to make a thorough study of the manner in which this might best be done. In the case cited above, the anthropologist would have suggested the following general steps:

1. Trial of several varieties of hybrid corn, with full recognition on the part of everyone that this was a test to discover which corn the people liked best.
2. Testing to see how the corn selected really fitted into the culture patterns.
3. Continued working with the farmers in order to see that they fully convinced themselves of the advantages of the new corn.
4. Continued contact to obviate all difficulties and to make any modifications that might be called for.

By such means, the problem which did arise might have been forestalled and met, and the society as a whole benefited.

Aware of the contribution which the anthropologist can make toward the solution of such problems, the United Nations, and the state departments of many countries are now increasingly calling upon the services of anthropologists. Governments are not only calling upon anthropologists to make studies of nonliterate peoples who will soon be coming under the influences of civilization, as in South America and in India, but they are also being called upon to make studies of peoples who have already been affected by the technologically more advanced societies. And the study of such peoples is not one iota less important than the study of nonliterate peoples.

The phenomenon of cultural transmission in process is known as *acculturation*, and the study of acculturation throws valuable light upon the physiology, as it were, of culture and of cultural change. The manner in which one culture influences another is no longer merely a matter of theoretical interest, but of the greatest practical value and importance. For if the peoples of the world are to come closer together, the processes that accomplish this with the greatest benefit accruing to all must be understood. This means that the processes of acculturation, of association, and of interaction between differing peoples must be studied, analyzed, scanned, and predicted. Studies of this kind have been under way for some years, and there cannot be the least doubt that they will prove of the utmost value when they come to be applied—as some of them have already—to the solution of practical problems. It is, for example, a matter of official record that studies made by anthropologists of Japanese culture and character before the conclusion of World War II greatly helped the occupying forces of Japan. The United Nations and the Point Four program now permanently employ anthropologists to deal with all those problems which fall within their competence.

In a world torn by racial misunderstanding and conflict, the contribution the anthropologist has to make is fundamental. As a student of man's mental processes, in all the forms in which he finds them, in living nonliterate and literate cultures, the anthropologist is in a position to put the problems of race in their proper perspective and to return the soundest possible answers—where answers are available. Because of his varied field experience with innumerable different peoples, the anthropologist is able to apply the results of that experience to the amelioration and solution of race problems.

Anthropologists are by no means agreed that there do not exist some differences in the mental capacities of some human groups as compared with others. But they are agreed that if such differences do exist, no matter what their nature, equality as an ethical principle in no way depends upon the assertion that human beings or human groups are, in fact, equal in endowment. The individual, no matter what ethnic group he may belong to, has to be considered as a person in his own right, if for no other reason than that he is a member of the human species. The anthropologist in the field knows better than anyone else possibly can that in every nonliterate group are to be found individuals of outstanding as well as mediocre ability—just as they are to be found in literate societies. And he also knows, and hopes to convince others, that the only reasonable way in which to discover what an individual's abilities are, is not to begin with a private or public prejudice, but to treat the individual as a person and provide him with all the opportunities which will enable him to maximize his potentialities. This is not only the most reasonable approach to the whole subject of race, but the scientific one, and the one that happens to correspond with the only possible democratic approach.

In discussing racial differences, this book has emphasized that in the vast majority of traits, physical and mental, the likenesses far outweigh the differences. In the course of the evolution of man, the principal complex of traits which have been at the highest premium are those which are still valued by all societies and by most individuals: the capacity to get along with others, the ability to cooperate, the wisdom to know when to hold one's tongue and when to loose it; in other words, the general trait which may be called plasticity or educability. This trait is the one which natural selection and social selection has most favored in all human societies throughout the long, secular period of man's evolution. It is unlikely that in the course of that evolution any particular mental traits were ever selected anywhere nearly as consistently as the trait of plasticity has been. It also appears unlikely that, with the great history of racial mixture which mankind as a whole has behind it, and with the exchange and intermixture of genes that has resulted, there can have been any driftage of genes causing significant differences to appear in mental ability. If driftage can be eliminated—and it appears that it can be because of the racial mixing that has occurred—from the history of the development of man's genetic potentialities for mental ability, it would seem highly unlikely that there really exist any significant differences in mental capacity for the different ethnic groups of mankind. This is not to deny that such differences *may* exist, but it is to assert that if such differences do exist, those best able to demonstrate their existence, namely, the anthropologists, have been unable to find any evidence for it.

As the UNESCO *Statement on Race* puts it: "It often happens that a national group may appear to be characterized by particular psychological attributes. The superficial view would be that this is due to race. Scientifically, however, we realize that any common psychological attribute is more likely to be due to a common historical and social background, and that such attributes may obscure the fact that, within different populations consisting of many human types, one will find approximately the same range of temperament and intelligence."

Indeed, it is the usual finding that when equal opportunities for the development of capacities are made available to members of different ethnic groups and their environments are equalized as much as possible, intelligence scores become equalized also. The achievements of nonliterate peoples, as the anthropologist in the field has come to know them, have usually evoked in him feelings of the highest respect.

If there are any lessons to be learned from what anthropology has to teach us, perhaps the most important of them all is that beneath all the differences in customs and body-form which human beings display, there exists a fundamental likeness, a likeness which far outweighs all the differences.

If some groups of humanity are culturally more advanced in some respects than others, it is because their opportunities have been greater, and not because of some supposed innate superiority. No group of human beings is of less value in the scale of humanity than any other, for all groups of human beings possess the potentialities for development which, under the proper environmental stimulation, would enable them to contribute maximally to the achievement of humanity.

Every culture can be regarded as the historic result of a people's attempt to adjust itself to its environment. Before the advent of the twentieth century, that environment was usually narrowly bounded. Today the boundaries which formerly separated people are crumbling before our eyes. Mankind is moving—in spite of occasional appearances to the contrary—toward unity without uniformity, toward the condition in which the differences that today separate men will grow to be regarded, not as causes for suspicion, fear, and discrimination, but as no more important than the differences which exist between the members of the same family. To that end, among others, the service of the anthropologist is dedicated.

Books for Further Reading

Asimov, Isaac, and Boyd, William C. *Races and People*. Abelard-Schuman, Ltd., New York, 1955.
A clear account of the mechanisms of inheritance as they relate to the differentiation of man.

Astrov, Margot (ed.). *The Winged Serpent*. The John Day Co., New York, 1946.
An anthology of American Indian prose and poetry of outstanding interest.

Bandi, Hans-Georg, and Maringer, Johannes. *Art in the Ice Age*. Frederick A. Praeger, Inc., New York, 1953.
A beautifully illustrated account of prehistoric art.

Benedict, Ruth. *Patterns of Culture*. Mentor Books, New American Library, New York, 1946.
A classic discussion of the meaning of culture as illustrated by four nonliterate cultures.

Childe, V. Gordon. *Man Makes Himself*. Mentor Books, New American Library, New York, 1952.
———. *What Happened in History*. Penguin Books, Inc., Baltimore, 1946.
Two books by a great English archaeologist which give an authoritative and well-told account of man's progress through the ages.

Coon, Carleton S. *The Story of Man*. Alfred A. Knopf, Inc., New York, 1954.
The best book for the layman on man from the first human being to primitive culture and beyond.

Dobzhansky, Theodosius. *Evolution, Genetics and Man*. John Wiley & Sons, Inc., New York, 1955.
An authoritative work on the mechanisms of evolution with especial reference to man.

Dunn, L. C., and Dobzhansky, Theodosius. *Heredity, Race and Society*. Mentor Books, New American Library, New York, 1952.
A scientific explanation of human differences.

Herskovits, Melville J. *Man and His Works: The Science of Cultural Anthropology*. Alfred A. Knopf, Inc., New York, 1948.
One of the best all-round textbooks on cultural anthropology.

Honigmann, John J. *Culture and Personality*. Harper & Brothers, New York, 1954.
An excellent account of the relationship of group membership and culture to personality.

Howells, William. *The Heathens: Primitive Man and His Religions*. Doubleday & Co., Inc., New York, 1948.
An able and readable account of primitive religion.

Kluckhohn, Clyde. *Mirror for Man: The Relationship of Anthropology to Modern Life*. Whittlesey House, McGraw-Hill Book Co., Inc., New York, 1949.
This is the best and most readable introduction to what the anthropologist tries to do.

Kroeber, Alfred L. *Anthropology: Race, Language, Culture, Psychology, Prehistory*. Harcourt, Brace & Co., New York, 1948.
The outstanding textbook on general anthropology.

La Barre, Weston. *The Human Animal.* The University of Chicago Press, Chicago, 1954.
A most interesting discussion of man from the unified standpoint of the cultural and physical anthropologist and depth psychologist.

Mead, Margaret. *New Lives for Old: Cultural Transformation—Manus, 1928–1953.* William Morrow & Co., New York, 1956.
An exciting restudy of the Manus Islanders after they had stepped from the Stone Age into the Air Age, showing, among other things, how speedily such a change can be made.

———— (ed.). *Cultural Patterns and Technical Change.* Mentor Books, New American Library, New York, 1954.
Originally published by UNESCO, this volume provides a fascinating series of accounts of different cultures in process of technical change.

Montagu, Ashley. *An Introduction to Physical Anthropology,* 2nd edition. Charles C Thomas, Springfield, Ill., 1951.
For the layman and beginning student, an introduction to the origin, evolution, and development of man as a physical organism.

————. *Man's Most Dangerous Myth: The Fallacy of Race.* 3rd edition. Harper & Brothers, New York, 1952.
A full discussion of the problems of race.

————. *The Direction of Human Development.* Harper & Brothers, New York, 1955.
On the nature of human nature.

Penniman, T. K. *A Hundred Years of Anthropology.* 2nd edition. The Macmillan Co., New York, 1952.
A history of anthropology up to 1952.

Radin, Paul. *Primitive Man As Philosopher.* Appleton-Century, New York, 1927. An extremely interesting and readable discussion of nonliterate man as a thinker.

Scheinfeld, Amram. *The New You and Heredity.* J. B. Lippincott Co., Philadelphia, 1950.
The best book for the layman on human inheritance.

Singer, Charles, Holmyard, E. J., and Hall, A. R. (eds.). *A History of Technology,* vol. 1. Oxford University Press, New York, 1954.
An authoritative account by experts of the technologies of man from the earliest times to the fall of ancient empires.

UNESCO. *The Race Question in Modern Science.* Whiteside, Inc. Books—UNESCO, William Morrow & Co., New York, 1957.
An authoritative and clear discussion of the various aspects of the race question by nine experts.

Index

Italic page numbers refer to illustrations.

ABOUT THE AUTHOR

ASHLEY MONTAGU was born in London, England, in 1905, and studied anthropology at the Universities of London and Florence, and Columbia University, where he was awarded the degree of Doctor of Philosophy for a thesis on the Australian aborigines. Professor Ashley Montagu has been scientific worker at the British Museum (Natural History), Curator of Physical Anthropology at the Wellcome Historical Medical Museum, London, Assistant Professor of Anatomy at New York University, Anthropologist to the Division of Child Research at the same university, Associate Professor of Anatomy at the Hahnemann Medical College and Hospital, Philadelphia, and Chairman and Professor of Anthropology, Rutgers University. He has also been a visiting lecturer and professor at Harvard University and the University of Delaware, Senior Lecturer in Anthropology on the Veterans Administration Postgraduate Training Program in Psychiatry and Neurology, and was Rapporteur of the UNESCO Committee of Experts on Race which drafted the famous UNESCO Statement on Race. He has been Family Affairs and Anthropological Adviser to NBC, and has appeared on many radio and television shows in his capacity as an anthropologist. He is Chairman of the Anisfield-Wolf Award Committee which awards annual prizes for meritorious works in the field of race relations, and he is an associate and advisory editor of *Isis* (The Journal of the History of Science), *Gemmologia* (the study of twins and twinning), and *Child-Family Digest*. Professor Ashley Montagu is a member of many scientific and learned societies, and is the author of some eighteen books, mostly in the field of anthropology. He has also contributed several hundred articles to the scientific and general periodicals of this and other countries. His hobbies are gardening and book collecting.

THIS BOOK WAS SET IN

BASKERVILLE AND CASLON TYPES BY

BROWN BROTHERS LINOTYPERS

THE PAPER IS PERKINS AND SQUIER COMPANY'S

RRR SMOOTH ANTIQUE

MADE BY P. H. GLATFELTER COMPANY

IT WAS PRINTED AND BOUND AT

THE PRESS OF THE WORLD PUBLISHING COMPANY

TYPOGRAPHY AND DESIGN ARE BY

LAWRENCE S. KAMP